JELLY BEANS
IN LIFE 2
TRAILS

DAVID
May the Jelly Beans
in your life always BE
Sweet!   SIC

by
Sig Schmalhofer

NOTES FROM THE AUTHOR

For the latest Jelly Bean news, please refer to
my website: www.jellybeansinlife.com or visit
Facebook.com/jellybeansinlife

May the Jelly Beans in your life always be sweet!

Sig Schmalhofer

JELLY BEANS IN LIFE 2 TRAILS

JELLY BEANS
IN LIFE 2
TRAILS

CHAPTER 1
"Trails in Life"

On a glorious day in the summer of 1993, Charlie, as he did every day, methodically set out to perform his afternoon scouting duties. The job entailed insuring that everything within his ranch domain was in order. In his younger days, the routine included a trip to the gazebo. But as he gracefully aged, climbing up and down the steep, slippery trail had become a struggle. Hence, that task was taken off his to-do list. However, he always made it a point to visit a giant sycamore, better known as the rattlesnake tree, making certain that no sidewinders were sunning beneath it.

The splashes of gray on Charlie's paws and whiskers added even more dignity than already graced him. As usual, he explored more than walked. He sniffed, raised his leg, and stuck his nose into any burrow or bush that might need to be investigated. He watched a lizard, boldly striped with yellow rings, scamper out of a gopher hole. Since the Labrador Retriever was at peace with these reptiles, he reacted with ears perked and nothing more.

He finally reached his destination, the red barn adjacent to Penny Lane, which was built when times were better. With friendly eyes and a gently wagging tail, Charlie greeted Sergeant Pepper, an aging, perceptive stallion that was now a permanent ranch resident. In his younger years Charlie's tail would aggressively snap to and fro when he was happy, but now it merely eased its way side to side. After all, there was no need to expend any unnecessary energy. As was the ritual, the stallion responded to the canine's greeting by kicking a fence railing.

Charlie lumbered towards his favorite spot, an inviting corner of paradise that featured hay bedding, shade, and a good view of ranch activity. As he plopped onto the cherished piece of real estate, the sensible horse neighed, as if to celebrate a simple joy in the lives of a dog and a horse — and the reassurance of knowing they were not alone. Charlie and Sergeant Pepper were like empty nesters who said little, but treasured the comfort of being in the same room together.

Over the years, the ranch had been celebrated as a harmonious corner of the earth, quietly tucked away on a road less traveled. But skirmishes were unavoidable. The thorn of a cactus in the skin of a mammal was a reminder that nature provides territorial balances that require respect. However, compatible four-legged residents shared the ranch with ease.

The barn's 'lean to' provided a popular getaway for two men whose character was the glue that cemented their friendship. Seated comfortably in lawn chairs and taking a break from the grind of their businesses, Larry Schafer, a sales rep who many of his customers called Ratchet-Ass, and Red Star, an urban cowboy plumbing contractor, pondered the trails in life that lay before them.

Larry started the conversation, "I just read an article in the paper."

"I'm sure you're talking about the piece Mary wrote on the local economy."

Larry raised his eyes as if he was seeking redemption from the heavens. "It's depressing to read about."

"Running a business is even worse!"

Larry shrugged. "You're right! This down-turn is flat wearing me out, but Mary did give you some free publicity!"

Red pretended to be annoyed, but his easy going nature was a dead giveaway, "Living with a journalist is interesting."

"I understand. There's never a dull moment being married to a school teacher either. Particularly when she double teams as a town council lightening rod."

"Sounds like you've read the many articles that reference Susan!"

Larry reflected, "I'm surrounded by celebrities!"

"I'm not interested in being famous. I just want my men to plumb houses."

Larry thought about the glow in the eyes of Red and Mary when they first met at Sal's. "It's been five years since the last town hall meeting on the moratorium. I'm guessing you guys are close to an anniversary."

"Neither one of us remembers the exact day we started living together."

"Really?"

"One thing just kind of led to another, and then another."

"So your relationship has been like a crossword puzzle."

"What?"

"One move provides a clue for the next one."

"You continue to be one amazing Ratchet!"

"Do you think you'll ever get married?"

"It's hard to say, we both have quirky tendencies. Getting married might knock the teeter totter out of kilter."

"Yeah, I get it."

After a moment of soul searching, Red remarked with a subject changer, "Where's my girl Candy?"

"Sorry Red, I thought you knew. The thin balance in my bank account dictated that I lay her off."

"Damn! I hope like hell she ends up back at the Flier's waiting tables."

"I hated to do it, but I just couldn't afford her."

"I get it! I get it! Downsizing is a real pisser. I've now lain off 700 plumbers; men that by all rights should be working."

Because Larry regretted opening a wound that hurt his friend, he attempted to ease the pain, "I know it hurts you to cut back. You're a proud man. But what choice do you really have? You're operating right here in Southern California's Inland Empire, the epicenter of the housing crash!"

"Exactly! Through most of the eighties, Town and Country did the plumbing on over 10,000 new houses a year. We'll be damn lucky to do 800 this year. To make things worse, we'll only do that many if we take the jobs at a loss. In this crash, reaching in my pocket is pretty much a given. Other than going broke, the only option I have is to keep a small crew working, minimize losses and ride out the storm."

Larry shook his head in affirmation. "It's frustrating to work harder than ever for less than nothing!"

"It's a bitch, but I'm sticking it out. I'm hanging onto the buzz words my builders are using; 'stay alive until 1995'."

"Haven't you saved enough money to ride your horse into the sunset and call it a day?"

"That time has come and gone. If I was going to shut down my shop, I should have done it three years ago. Now I'm in too deep!"

Larry nodded. "That sounds familiar. When your business suffers, so does mine. Every contractor in the new construction business is struggling, which in turn trickles down to me. Now that I've laid-off Candy, I'm wondering if I should cut back some more and become a one-man band. It makes financial sense, but it's a huge territory. I'd pretty much be living in my van. Plus, I'd have to convince $PROH_2O$ that I could still cover the market. Since they're my lifeline, it would be a risky proposition. Commissioned independent reps live and die with 30 day contracts."

Red replied skeptically, "I know you love your tired Astro, but if you're planning on driving up and down half of the highways in the state of California, you might think about investing in reliable transportation."

"You're right, but a car payment is the last thing I need. I'm not sure what I should do. I just don't know!"

"It doesn't sound like you're wiggling your toes much."

Larry was puzzled. "What?"

"After a rough day, I kick off my boots, wiggle my toes and think about the good old days!"

"You have a way of finding easy solutions for puzzling issues."

"For me, toe wiggling is like taking a ride in my truck on a back road with the windows open while John Denver sings 'Country Roads'."

"I need to think about that. You may have a point there."

"Good!"

"I wish I knew where the trail I'm on is headed. I think maybe Susan suspects I'm on a dead end. She kind of understands my business, but when it comes down to it, she really doesn't get it. And then there's me! There are days I think I'll make it, and other days where I worry that I'll be buried beneath an avalanche of unconnected dots. I guess that means I don't really get it either."

"A guy who can tie together loose ends is ahead of the game. But I've yet to meet the man that doesn't let some shit fall between the cracks."

"I used to think I was the guy who could cover all the bases, but now I've got a gazillion dots bouncing in my head that just aren't connecting."

"You're dialing a wrong number! You should be talking with Susan. I'm a cowboy plumber, not a shrink!"

Larry silently stewed before replying, "I keep waiting for the timing to be right to have the conversation, but just when I think that moment has arrived, we take a detour."

"Maybe you're dancing around the stuff you should be dealing with head on!"

"I think it would be easier to talk if I didn't feel like the dots in my head are about to explode."

"If you're not careful, the avalanche of questions you're wrestling with will bury your ass in your empty barrel of answers!"

"We started having a good, heart to heart talk the other night, but then she hit me with her theory that weeds are just plants that happen to grow in the wrong place."

"You're absolutely killing me, Larry!"

"Look around here, Red. There are weeds everywhere. It makes me crazy."

"Joe was a big help to you."

"He helped me with everything. He unloaded and stacked hay for us with ease. Plus he was my weed terminator. Since I can't afford him anymore, weeds are popping up all over the ranch. It's a hostile takeover."

"Weed terminator? Weed hostile takeover? Really? You amaze me! What do weeds have to do with the shit we're talking about?"

"I guess my confusion is confusing you."

"Ratchet! Get yourself off of whatever trail you wandered onto! Susan is a good woman. You're damn lucky to have her!"

"I know that!"

"You do? I don't think you have a clue. You really don't get it!"

"Get what?"

"That Susan's been saddled with the near impossible job of keeping your ass on a straight and narrow trail."

"Okay already!"

"And think about it! Does it really matter whether or not that trail has weeds?"

Larry offered nothing but a frustrated nod. Both men paused to take slow, refreshing sips of lemonade. Giant sycamore trees, proud and strong, framed the vista. Cactus, geraniums and even weeds painted a vibrant masterpiece. That splendor plus a gentle breeze flavored with the fragrance of orange blossoms should have given both men every reason to celebrate life. But in the midst of the worst economic challenge of their lives, it was easy to get lost in a vast maze of unconnected dots.

Red offered a ray of hope, "Ratchet, we'll figure it out; one way or another. I'm not sure how, but we will! There's always a way. We just need to find it!"

"I hope so."

"Aren't you the guy who can find a jelly bean in a jar full of sour balls?"

Larry affirmed Red's assessment, responding with an injection of determination, "You make a good point. The *Jelly Beans in Life* have been good to me! I guess I'm just having a bad day. So what do you think?"

"I think you'll figure stuff out. Maybe you should start by reminding Susan that she's not alone. When she gets tired of dragging your big ass in the right direction, she can always call me. I'll saddle up and give her a helping hand. You're reinforcing something I already knew."

"What's that?"

"It seems like it takes every cowboy in town to herd you down the right trail."

"I've always been a guy who seeks out his own trails."

"Maybe that's the problem. If you keep picking wrong trails, you'll wander off a cliff. You need to get back to noodling on a pad of paper and figuring shit out. We all have dots to connect! That's a given! But you're elevating the head scratching to a new level!"

Whenever Larry found himself losing sight of the *Jelly Beans in Life*, he would rely on his favorite tools: a sharp pencil and a yellow pad of paper. After isolating himself from the clutter of outside distractions, he would brainstorm until clarity and direction emerged from scribbled thoughts, columns of numbers or random notations. But, as the trails in life beat him down, Larry's sharp pencil had unwittingly rolled off his desk, hiding in a hidden corner. His yellow pad was apparently lost beneath a mound of unconnected dots.

Larry paused to soak in Red's advice. "What's wrong with me? You're right! I do need to find my lost pencil, sharpen it, and grab ahold of a friendly pad of paper!"

Silence took the stage while Red searched for the words to further inspire his friend. "While you're racking your brain with that pencil, try like hell to get your arms wrapped around a couple of things…"

"My dot connecting antenna is up!"

Red removed his hat and fanned his overheated freckled face. "Well, the first one's a no-brainer. In fact, we've kind of been talking about it. But because you're so screwed up, I think it's worth repeating."

After wiping the sweat dripping down his cheek, Red continued, "You need to figure out where in the hell you want to end up and then take the trail that has the best shot at getting you there!"

"That's great, but that's easier said than done."

"Damn it, Ratchet! If you'll just let me finish, maybe you'll grab ahold of something you can noodle with."

Red paused before continuing, "Just remember that for some unexplainable reason that defies all logic, there actually are people in your life that give a rat's ass about you. If you'll just let them, they just might help you stay off slippery paths headed in the wrong damn direction, and guide you to the trails that will allow you to kick off your boots, wiggle your toes and start connecting the dots lost inside your square head!"

Larry was speechless, which in itself was remarkable.

Red eased his way out of his chair and stretched. It was time to follow the Lake Mathias trail that would lead him to his ranch, ten minutes away. He swayed his stiff body from side to side then shook Larry's hand. "Ratchet, since you have a strong mind for thinking up trails of bullshit and a weak back for lifting bales of hay, call me when your load arrives and I'll give you a hand."

Larry shrugged, "We'll be okay."

"There you go again, you dumb ass! You just won't accept help without a fight. Do you have any idea how painful it is to watch you ratchet yourself step by step?"

"I guess I missed that movie."

"Congratulations! You actually said something that makes sense."

"I did?"

"Well, maybe. I need to make a video of you walking; well, kind of walking. That way, you'll see for yourself what the rest of us are watching with dumbfounded amazement!"

"So you're saying I have entertainment value?"

As Red mounted his horse, 'Lucky', and settled into his saddle, he summed up a head scratching afternoon. "You are such a piece of work! A big ass piece of work!"

Larry smiled. What else could he do? But he did reply as only Larry would, "The trails in life have connected your business to mine and you to me!"

Red slowly rode away from the world of Larry being Larry, mumbling cowboy profanities to himself. It was the tail end of a long, hot day and the conversation with his exasperating friend only served to raise the temperature. Red instinctively gripped the reins a bit tighter as he headed home, down the familiar horse trail. Searching for clarity in a muddled Larry world, Red gently patted his horse on the head and commented, "Lucky, I'm exhausted! Damn exhausted! Why in the hell does Ratchet insist on ratcheting me until I feel like my guts are gonna bust wide open?"

"Dr. M"

Sensing it was getting close to dinner time, Charlie caught up with Larry as he slowly walked up Penny Lane's steep driveway. Reaching the top, their huffing and puffing got the attention of Susan, who was standing in front of her sports car, cute as a chipmunk, with teacup elbows formed by the hands on both of her shapely hips. Her dress matched the signet red color of the vintage '55 Corvette. Because Susan meticulously cared for it, the classic looked as if it had just been driven off the dealer showroom. There was no doubt that both Susan and the Corvette were timeless beauties.

"Looks like Penny Lane squeezed every gram of energy out of both of you. Since our delivery of hay is arriving Saturday, perhaps we should hire some help to unload it."

As he gasped for air, Larry replied, "Red said he'd help us. I'll let him know."

"Red is terrific! Do you have any idea how lucky you are to have that man as a friend?"

"I think you two are double-teaming me. I just got an earful from Red about how lucky I am to have you."

"And what did you say?"

"I agreed of course!"

"I know you're a salesman and you're trying to sell me something, but I'm not buying it!"

"Maybe you're missing my irresistible charm."

Susan smiled as she replied, "Sometimes it's better to ignore your antics. By the way, Mayor Sam is dropping by."

"The Mayor and his '53 Chevy! That combination will be written about in history books one day! What are you two cooking up now?"

"Nothing special, but as you know, July is upon us."

"Sounds like the moratorium and the 'Susan Schafer plan' will again be center stage."

"It will be déjà vu all over again!"

"Another town hall meeting and vote?"

"I'm afraid so."

Larry finally caught his breath. "Don't you think a renewal is a slam dunk?"

"Maybe, but I just want to make sure I leave no stone unturned!"

"I think you learned the importance of being prepared when you were a girl scout."

"You really are a charmer tonight. But that aside, I'm worried about you. It seems you're laboring more and more with each step you take. I just watched you and Charlie walk up the driveway. Charlie is about 100 years old in dog years, so I understand him struggling, but you are still a young man. You really should have yourself checked out."

The chugging sound of Sam's '53 Chevy interrupted the conversation.

Sam put an exclamation mark on his arrival by honking his horn three times in rapid fire succession. After climbing out of his cherished sedan, he waddled at about Larry's speed, but he was now almost twice Larry's age. Sam still wore red suspenders to keep his pants from falling, but they no longer stretched over a proud belly. A new doctor in Riverside had designed a program that got Sam in the best shape of his life. Not only did Dr. M have remedies for a myriad of ailments, he taught his patients how the parts that make up the human body work together in harmony, or conflict. Once Sam understood his own body and fed it the nutrients it needed, he was rejuvenated.

Sam served up his trademark greeting, "It's a beautiful day to be alive!"

Susan gave him a big hug and led the trio, plus Charlie, to the kitchen. She cheerfully turned to Sam. "I can offer you fresh squeezed lemonade or a glass of wine."

"If I wasn't driving home, I'd have a glass of wine instead of the lemonade. I now make a habit of drinking a glass merlot every evening. Dr. M believes wine is one of the keys to health and longevity. But, don't get me wrong, this lemonade is delightful."

Susan rolled her eyes. "We do have a guest room, Sam."

Sam tugged on his suspenders. "That's quite alright, I'm a creature of habit, and one of my favorite rituals is sleeping in my own bed, with my own pillow, in my own humble cottage."

The friends took their seats on the patio. The sun was low in the west and the evening breeze was as refreshing as the lemonade they were drinking. In five years the economy had turned upside down, but the view of the lake and the purple mountains in the horizon were majestically unchanged.

As Mayor Sam tapped the glasses of Larry and Susan, he proposed a toast that filled the ranch deck with elegance and emotion. "Evenings like this make me yearn to take more steps down my trail in life. I believe that Dr. M's program will add those steps."

Susan smiled. "I think you must be eating too many fruits and nuts, Sam. I can't even talk to you about budgets and horse trails without you beaming about the magic you have found with your new doctor. Let's talk about the big council meeting. Do you think we need to prepare a compelling argument or do you think an easy extension is in the works?"

Sam slowly and confidently replied, "Susan, Dr. M is the miracle on 12th Street, but your 'SS' Program is the miracle on Penny Lane. Yes indeed, the transformation of this town due to your plan is a miracle in its own right. If we did anything to change it, there would be a revolution in our township. Folks, of course, wish that the trails were ramping up quicker, but the pragmatic citizens among us know that we need to build the network within our means."

Larry added his perspective, "You two have made Lake Mathias very special. This piece of paradise is an island in the middle of an economic storm. My business is suffering for sure and so is just about everyone else in the construction industry. The only shiny penny in my entire territory is Lake Mathias."

Susan interjected, "I read all about it in Mary's article."

"When I'm with Mary, I'm careful about what I say. You never know what might make its way into the newspaper."

"That's unfair, Sam. Mary has a mighty pen but would never hurt her friends."

"Yes indeed, it really is a beautiful day to be alive."

Susan's moratorium compromise had transformed the sleepy town of Lake Mathias into a destination popular for any cowboy or cowgirl who ever mucked manure out of a corral and smiled while they were doing it. The town was no longer just another rock buried at a quarry. It had been transformed into the precious gem sparkling within a field of dust and tumbleweeds.

Sam never overstayed his welcome; never visiting longer than the time it took him to drink one glass of a refreshment. As he took his last sip, he stood and reached out to shake Larry's hand. A quick hug from Susan and he was off and running: Sam and his beloved '53, heading down the driveway and disappearing into the peaceful calm of a Lake Mathias evening.

Mayor Sam's visit had provided a peaceful rest stop on the trail of the lives of Larry and Susan. But the break from reality was over and now it was time to tackle the rocky footing ahead.

As they walked back into the kitchen, Charlie whined and Susan took a deep breath. "Yes Charlie, I'll feed you right now." As she filled Charlie's bowl, her eyes opened wide and caught Larry's attention. "I'm scared. Is Connection Sales going to make it?"

"We'll be okay."

"But Larry, you are down to just two employees."

"Since we're a couple of years away from a recovery, I'm staying flexible. I might have to lay off Billy or Emily; maybe both. I'm just not sure. I do know that the long hours don't bother me and I'm committed to doing whatever it takes. We had one really good year before the crash, so I know that with even a little cooperation from the economy, I can make Connection Sales into something very special."

"I know it's tough out there. I know you're giving it all you've got. But at some point in time you need to wave a white flag and acknowledge that you're on a dead end trail!"

"The commissions we earn from PROH$_2$O faucets are down. Way down! Since the home building business is cyclical and the faucet business is tied to new housing, an agency like mine will struggle in a housing crash. In a nutshell, that's the challenge I'm wrestling with!"

Susan sighed, "That's exactly why I'm worried!"

"But you're missing the jelly beans in this scenario!"

Susan raised her eyebrows and shook her head while Larry continued, "The plumbing business, as a whole, because of the repair and replacement market, is typically steady. As Connection Sales gets more established, we'll attract manufacturers whose products do not rely on new construction."

"Our pockets aren't deep! I just worry that you're the captain of a sinking ship that will take you, me and the ranch down with it."

"This economy is a head scratcher that demands every ounce of resolve I can muster up, but there are still trails to success out there. I just need to find them."

"Larry, you and Mayor Sam are romantic dreamers that believe in miracles. I see life through logical eyes."

If Larry had carved out time to fill a notepad with clarity before having this conversation, the war of words may have been different. But lacking a feasible plan with more substance, he responded with a defensive strike, "Susan, you're a pessimist!"

"That is absolutely untrue: I'm a realist. And, I'll add that I'm definitely concerned with you climbing the stairs that lead to your office in the barn. I'm worried that you have something more serious going on inside of your square head and round body — something that you're not sharing with me."

Larry paused before cautiously dipping his toe into a stormy sea. "Is that all you're worried about?"

"No, I also worry about the moratorium coming to a head, yet again. I don't think I've quite recovered from the sign campaign that attacked me last time. Sam is worried about adding a few steps to the trail in his life. I'm worried to death about every pebble and every turn."

Larry took a huge breath. After a painfully slow exhale he uttered a simple refrain, "I understand!"

Like animals seeking shelter after a bolt of lightning, Larry the hopeless romantic and Susan the perceptive realist, buried their vulnerable emotions into one another's arms. That hug, in spite of their differences, reconfirmed the love that resided deep within their hearts. As they embraced, they exchanged loving pats on the back. After their bodies separated, Larry offered a smile and a comment that he didn't really believe himself, "Don't worry. I promise you everything will be just fine!"

Susan quickly discarded Larry's attempt to smooth out a turbulent landing. "Even you don't believe those words. I'm a sucker for a loving squeeze that makes me happy that we're together, but I'm still not convinced that Romeo and Juliet will live happily ever after."

"They didn't?"

"Nice try Larry. If I had just one or two small things that were bothering me, I guess I could toss them aside, but right now my mind is swirling and I'm worried sick about everything."

Larry winked his right eye and shrugged before replying, "I know the trail won't be easy for either one of us. But let's find joy in the experience. The trails in life are to be embraced, not feared."

"What am I to do with you? You are such a romantic dreamer. You're trying to cover up the fact that you have no idea where you're going, let alone how you will get there. I'm beginning to think that in addition to a doctor that evaluates you physically, you may need a physician that analyzes whatever it is that's going on in your head."

Unconnected dots flew around Larry's head like rose petals in a tornado. "You're right! I need to figure stuff out! I need to noodle with a sharp pencil and a blank tablet to develop a strategy, a plan that will allow me to connect the dots that are driving you and me crazy. You said I'm a hopeless romantic. A romantic? Yes! Hopeless? No! I just need to find a trail that leads me somewhere, not just anywhere. That's the world I've always lived in, the trail in life I've always traveled! When I saw you standing next to your Corvette this afternoon, I was reminded that, not that long ago at Ventura College, I followed the same kind of romantic trail. The trail that led me to a life with you!"

CHAPTER 3

"Atom Smashers"

I t was still dark when Larry eased his way down Penny Lane to his barnyard office. He made the trek on his own because there was no way that Charlie was going to uncoil and struggle to his feet at this hour of the morning. After all, not even the sun would make an appearance for another hour. Susan was on summer vacation, taking a break from an unrelenting alarm clock. She was on a dreamy journey through the strawberry fields in her life.

Larry's morning barn routine always started with the preparation of that very first pot of coffee. The very first taste from the first cup was something that Larry always looked forward to. In two minutes the aroma of the Brazilian coffee beans would fill his inner soul. The steaming hot brew would be poured into his prized Ventura coffee mug: a masterpiece adorned with blue waves, a surfboard, and a red Woodie parked casually on the sand.

Now Larry opened the squeaky top half of the Dutch farmhouse door. This served as a wake-up call for a compassionate stallion whom Larry nicknamed, 'The Sarge'. Sergeant Pepper was old, but the lure of jelly beans insured his prompt appearance opposite Larry. The horse's massive head filled the upper door opening, and his brown eyes begged for a treat. Larry pulled a handful of jelly beans out of his pocket and watched as the Sarge mushed them down.

"If you ever tell Susan that I'm feeding you jelly beans, you'll end up sharing this barn with a new boarder. Anyway, I really need to move my office downstairs. Those steps are torturous. I don't understand why, but they are. When I played football in high school, I ran up and down bleacher stairs at practice for an hour without a problem, but now, when I walk up Penny Lane, I feel like I'm 91."

As Larry's mind slipped back to high school, The Sarge opened his eyes wide and stood his ears at attention.

"My boyhood dream was to be a star quarterback. I could throw a spiral tighter, further and straighter than anyone in the neighborhood. In spring practice I was listed as the first string quarterback. I was certain that I was on the road to becoming a football hero. I would be transformed from a typical anybody to a special somebody. Girls would head towards me instead of around me. But sadly, reality trumped fantasy. The passing drills were over. Now it was time to get down to business. I listened intently to the coach. The next play called for me to carry the ball around 'right end' in a full sprint. I still remember the coach barking, 'Run, Schafer, run'. As I gasped for air, I screamed back a weak rebuttal, 'I am running'! The coach was stern and unemotional; he simply made a note on his clipboard that my full speed was about half the speed required to be the team's quarterback."

The Sarge expressed his empathy by delivering an aggressive whack onto the lower half of the Dutch door with his right hoof.

Larry continued telling his story to the captive audience, "Since the Berry Hill High School 'Atom Smashers' never threw a single pass all year, the coach's response was not surprising: 'Put that kid on the line'. That was the beginning of my short, torturous football career which landed all 160 pounds of me into the role as a third string lineman for a small high school and into oblivion. The number 7 that I wore as a quarterback was replaced with a 73. Linemen wore big two digit numbers that stretched around their massive bulging torsos. My uniform was draped on me like a limp rag hanging over a faucet spout. The 7 and 3 didn't proudly stretch: they drooped."

The Sarge neighed.

"However, the coach did find a very important job for me. I knew it was important because I was reminded of how important it was at the beginning of each and every practice. My important job was to serve as the human tackling dummy for the all-state lineman, Igor Krakeldorf, who was huge, strong, and mean. Igor was the star of the team. To show Igor how much he was appreciated, the coach screamed at him from the very second he stepped onto the field until the moment he walked off of it. The number 99 stretched so tightly on his jersey that the nines wrapped around to his well-padded sides. I nicknamed him 'Igor the Carnivore', but not to his face. Since being Igor's tackling dummy did not make me popular with the girls, I desperately wanted to quit football for an activity more rewarding and less punishing. Being a quitter, however, was just not in my DNA.

"Then came the fateful day my football career happily, but painfully, came to an end. In an effort to discover his breaking point, the coach rode Igor even harder than usual, resulting in the Carnivore taking it out on me. When his monster shoulders plowed into me, I felt like Wylie Coyote after he is run over by a freight train. As they carried me off on a stretcher in agonizing pain and delirium, I managed a smile."

Sergeant Pepper shook his head east and west.

"Let me tell you why, Sarge. Like a soldier wounded on the battlefield, an injured football player is granted an honorary discharge which allows the maintenance of dignity. The torn ligaments in my knee, a broken nose that bloodied my face, and a concussion did the trick.

"Anyway, I didn't earn a letterman's jacket, but I do have an everlasting memory of the coach screaming at Igor, 'Great hit, Krakeldorf! That's the kind of intensity I've been looking for! Tighten up your chin strap son, and dedicate yourself to maintaining that high level of energy. If you find the inner strength to accomplish that, we'll win Friday night's game against the Anteaters!

"As the siren of the ambulance exploded into my ears, I remember feeling really sorry for the Anteaters, who were unaware of the destruction and carnage that 'the Carnivore' was capable of when he is tormented by the ranting of a psychotic coach. More importantly, I felt really lucky to escape the wrath of Igor Krakeldorf alive; worse for the wear, but nonetheless alive. I wasn't sure the Anteaters would be able to say the same thing. But, that was their worry, certainly not mine. Quietly I said to myself, 'Larry Schafer, you are no quitter!' That lesson still ricochets around my square head as I struggle to keep Connection Sales alive and keep my heavy legs moving forward!"

The Sarge responded with a confirming head shake as Larry turned away to re-fill his Ventura coffee mug, take a small sip, and place the cup on his desk. As he thought about the busy day ahead of him, he used the bannister to pull himself up the stairs, methodically climbing step by step. His legs moved as if he had sand bags tied to his ankles. After huffing and puffing to the top, Larry packed a box full of files and assorted office materials. He exhaustingly carried it downstairs to Candy's old office, which had just become his new office. He then trudged back up to gather his briefcase. It would take five more trips to complete the move.

The first order of business was to sort through the faxes that were received during the night. There were twenty-three coiled up as if they had been spring loaded. If Larry did not re-roll each one in the opposite direction, they would be impossible to read. There were two orders for faucets, two shipping acknowledgements, six requests for quotations, and ten memos from $PROH_2O$ and Connection's other small factories.

When Candy ran the office, she answered the phone and processed the faxes. But now Larry covered the office part time, made sales calls on the largest contractors and wholesalers in the territory, plus supervised the activities of his two outside sales people. In his spare time, he paid the bills, handled payroll, and kept the books. An unmanned office meant that callers would leave messages on Connection's answer machine, page Larry, or just hang-up in frustration.

After pricing and forwarding the orders to $PROH_2O$, Larry returned the requests for quotations. He then stuffed the faxed memos into a folder and slid it into his briefcase. Those memos he would read in small windows of time that opened up during his crammed days. Larry was always on the lookout for a phone, a restaurant, or a surprise pocket of time to catch up. Being stuck at a railroad crossing was a perfect example of utilizing good time management to review faxed memos.

The first phone call of the day came ringing in, "Connection Sales!"

"Larry, this is Emily."

Before Connection Sales, Emily Baker worked as a direct factory sales person for $PROH_2O$. Larry was her boss. When $PROH_2O$ elected to replace their factory sales force with an independent rep firm, Larry negotiated a contract with $PROH_2O$ for his fledgling company, Connection Sales, to handle the sales and marketing for $PROH_2O$ in Southern California. Emily never regretted her decision to go to work for Larry. Their relationship, based on mutual trust, had developed nicely over the years. She was fiercely competitive. She made up for her lack of technical knowledge with a commitment to working long hours with a smile. Emily was in the powerful position of being professional, reliable, and cute.

"Good morning."

"I'm headed to Santa Maria to work the central coast for a couple of days. If something crazy-urgent comes up in L.A., do you mind covering for me?"

"Of course not! I will be happy to do it! Write some business up there. We could sure use it."

"Got it boss! I'll be sure to tell our customers that you're going to fire me if I don't produce orders."

"Stay away from that line. You're a horrible liar."

That call completed, the phone rang again. "Connection Sales!"

"I sure liked it better when Candy answered the phone."

"So did I Billy. What's up?"

Billy Ray was a mad man. Larry's biggest management tasks involved cleaning up problems that Billy always seemed to be in the middle of. Customers either loved Billy or hated him. A customer in Victorville once hid behind his desk when he saw Billy pull into the parking lot. Larry was certain that the term 'loose cannon' came to being in the wake of an emergency clean-up of a Billy Ray sales disaster. He always had an agenda of issues. Most were self-inflicted; some as small as a pesky fruit fly, while others were as large as the man himself. Billy excitedly proceeded, "I really, really need to talk to you!"

"Okay."

"First off, is there any way you can send me some PROH$_2$O warranty forms? I'm out!"

Larry was all too familiar with this kind of a request. "Why are you always out of everything?"

Billy stammered, "Ah, well, I don't know."

Larry took a deep breath, "Okay, no problem, I'll take care of it. However, I'll remind you that it's your responsibility to order the forms directly from the factory."

"I know, I know."

Larry knew better but had to ask, "Is there anything else?"

"The factory is sabotaging me. All of our shower valves are leaking on the Desert Flowers job."

Larry had spent much of his career squeezing single ounces of truth out of rivers filled with lies. "I hope you don't believe all those valves are leaking, Billy. Sounds to me like a typical case of an agitated plumber with a wild imagination and propensity for exaggeration. By any chance, is Mel's Plumbing doing that job?"

"Ah, yeah"

"That figures. Mel always has problems. If the problem is widespread, he probably forgot to remove the cartridges before he did his soldering. If that's the case, the cartridges are fried!"

Billy hastily answered, "I'll check it out and let you know."

"Thanks Billy. It would be really great if you could squeeze in some time to write some business. I'll remind you that our agency's income is dependent on commissions."

"10-4 boss."

Larry's mind drifted away from his pressing schedule and thought about his long friendship with Billy Ray. Billy had spent his entire life bull doggedly sniffing out leads in a successful sales career. Even though he had earned more money than he ever would spend, he fought for every order as if he needed the business to merely survive. Larry and Billy were friends who had mutual respect for one another. Billy was a disaster in every sense of the word, yet he was tenaciously loyal and impeccably honest. His formidable body was a comfortable home for a huge heart. Whenever screw-ups outweighed his positive contributions, Billy miraculously closed a big deal that seemingly came from nowhere.

Larry moved back to the job at hand: organizing his thoughts, handling paperwork, and finalizing the day's schedule. There was no time to unpack the box from upstairs, but Larry did take time to make notes in his planner. Those notes would serve as his roadmap for the day. On his 'to-do list' he noted the calls that needed to be returned later in the day.

Since his first scdriverheduled appointment was at 7AM, Larry poured a cup of coffee to go, turned the coffee maker off, and grabbed his briefcase. His blue Astro van looked sad and tired. Sam's old '53 Chevy was a classic. Larry's Astro was just plain old and begged for a scrapyard retirement. Red urged him to replace it, but it was unlikely that would happen anytime soon. Connection Sales was in no shape to buy anything, let alone a new car. The hope was that somehow the Astro would stay mobile until business came out of its long slumber. Larry climbed into the captain's chair, using the steering wheel to pull himself into his seat. When he first bought the Astro, he slid into the van without a thought. Now the process was deliberate and calculated.

Larry vowed to put his challenges behind him. After all, there were things to do, places to go, and people to see. He took a deep breath and sipped another drink of hot brew. As he exited through Penny Lane's gates, he reminded himself that he was not a quitter. After all, that would have been proven when he was getting his atoms smashed by Igor the Carnivore. It seemed to him that the housing crash and Igor Krakeldorf were twin brothers, steadfastly intent on slamming him to the ground.

When Larry first started Connection Sales his goal was to build a successful company. Now his sights were riveted on staying viable. Larry, like Red, was a proud man. Failing was not an option. On the outside he seldom let down his guard, projecting a positive, jelly bean, attitude. On the inside, his blood boiled and his stomach churned. A sharp pain in his chest was a constant reminder that Connection Sales was teetering on the edge of extinction. Larry was confident that a return to business normalcy would remedy all of these ailments. As for his mobility issues, he said very little to Susan, but, he too, was concerned about the trail he was on. His legs were tired and heavy every single day. On other days his back hurt so bad that he forgot how heavy his legs really were. Meanwhile, the finances of Connection Sales were tighter than 36" slacks on his 42" body. Connection Sales was on a trail that would ultimately separate winners from losers. However, for Larry Schafer, losing was not an option!

CHAPTER 4

"The Pencil Breaker"

Larry arrived at Sunnymeade Pipe and Supply on 'Standard Larry Time', fifteen minutes before his 7 AM appointment. The first order of business was tackling problems: inspecting allegedly defective faucets. There were eight faucets in the bone pile, primitively marked NFG (No...Flipping...Good). Larry's translation, they were abused not defective. Real issues would have been marked with specific information. NFG faucets typically had no putty on their body, making it obvious they had never been installed. They were likely returned after getting beat up from bouncing around in the bed of a contractor's truck. Larry made a note to talk to Brenda Wright, the general manager and purchasing agent, about the rash of NFGs.

The next order of business was inventory management. 'CARDEX' was the manual, pre-computer system many wholesalers still used in 1993. Every inventoried item was issued a data card that was used to track purchase and sales history. Cards were organized by manufacturer in a drawer's hinged holder. A library of drawers was manually updated by a clerk every time there was a transaction. Cards were located by flipping through the hinged cards in a product line's drawer.

Salesmen like Larry, on their scheduled rounds, verified card accuracy for all the items within the product line they represented with a fiscal inventory. This led to their reward: writing a purchase order to replenish stock. Counting inventory, entering the data on the cards, and tidying up the stacks of product was a three-hour grind. There were reps that made a day out of this tedious chore and still fouled things up.

Larry tackled the tasks efficiently and always offered a smile. In addition to listing quantities and prices on the purchase order, he would indicate discounts, terms, and freight considerations plus use quoted net pricing for product earmarked for projects. To ensure proper handling, Larry would also process special orders, cross referencing them to the wholesaler's customer. Finally he would take the tedious paperwork to

Brenda, who would review and sign it.

Brenda liked Larry because he was friendly, efficient, and reliable. She would tenaciously audit the inventory count and order suggestions made by some reps because they would invariably make counting errors, suggest questionable reorder quantities, or screw up the pricing. But Larry's work was spot on and made Brenda's job easy.

The purchase orders were written in pencil to enable erased corrections. After being signed by the customer, they were faxed to the factory.

Larry finally reached the stage where he would receive his reward. Brenda signed the purchase order and was about to hand Larry his copy when her boss, Karl Tiff, abruptly entered the office.

"Brenda, what in the hell are you doing?"

Brenda, all too familiar with Karl's frequent temper tantrums, replied confidently, "I'm placing an order with Larry for $PROH_2O$ faucets."

Karl barked out commands in drill sergeant fashion, "Let me have that order and your pencil!"

A frustrated Brenda followed instructions reluctantly, wearing a scowl on her face. Sunnymeade Pipe and Supply was one of fourteen wholesale branches that were corporately owned by an investment company. Karl was the man in charge.

Karl grabbed Larry's hard-earned purchase order and methodically ripped it into quadrants. He then broke Brenda's pencil in half and deposited it, as well as the remnants of the purchase order, on her desk. "As of right now, you have a zero budget for buying."

Brenda was undeterred. "But we are low on $PROH_2O$. All of our contractors want to buy Larry's faucets."

Karl grumbled, "Transfer in from other branches whatever you can get your hands on and switch the balance of the business to Alpha. We are overstocked on Alpha Faucets!"

Larry looked at Brenda in disbelief. Karl eyed a stack of blank purchase orders in a tray. He pointed a determined finger at Brenda and demanded, "Give me those POs!"

Brenda complied.

Karl snarled, "Now hand over the POs hidden in your bottom drawer!" Brenda reached down and handed Karl a second stack.

As she rolled her eyes, she responded in a measured, controlled voice, "Karl. I am the buyer. How can I do my job without purchase orders?"

As Karl stormed out of the office, he barked, "Exactly!"

Brenda took a deep breath as she shook her head and replied to Larry, "Don't worry about it. Karl will probably be in my office next week and ask me about our $PROH_2O$ inventory. I will just smile at him. He has no idea that I keep a supply of purchase orders hidden above my desk in the ceiling."

"Really?"

Brenda pointed at an acoustic tile above her head. "I stand on my desk and slide the tile over. I've become an expert at it. I had to resort to this tactic last summer after Karl went on a rampage and turned my office upside down before he found all my hidden purchase orders. My ceiling stash is a secret.

"That's crazy!"

"Karl constantly preaches that we are buying way too much and not selling nearly enough. I fight back! I remind him that it's hard to sell product we don't have!"

Larry was baffled and discouraged. Brenda was evidently accustomed to Karl's tactics and took it all in stride. She winked at Larry and offered a consolation prize, "If you need a phone, you can use the desk next door."

"Isn't that Jimmy Wilson's office?"

"Not anymore. We no longer have a sales manager. Karl fired Jimmy yesterday. Get the picture?"

Larry nodded, sheepishly turned, and headed towards the office next door. Before entering Jimmy's office, he stopped to find some sense of clarity in what had become a very dark, foggy morning. He thought about Red's comment: "Stay alive until 1995". The brutality of the economic climate had claimed another victim. Larry reminded himself that Jimmy had a drinking problem which likely contributed to his demise. He sat down to gather his thoughts and get caught up with the business of managing Connection Sales. After dealing with the calls left on his answer machine, he thumbed through the faxed memos that had arrived overnight. The abuse of Igor Krakeldorf and Karl Tiff were incidental contact compared with the fax message that abruptly put Larry in a daze. Simultaneously his pager, which had been quiet, began a train wreck of beeps. His heart seemed to beat in rhythm with the vibrations.

"Effective immediately, the assets of $PROH_2O$ have been purchased by Xin Din Industries. More information will be forthcoming, but new ownership anticipates no further changes to the organization."

Larry had learned early in his career that when a larger company buys a smaller one, an immediate announcement, typically a lie, is issued stating that new ownership intends to operate with a "business as usual" approach.

Because of that, Larry sat in a quiet depression, head slumped, fingers fidgeting. As blood rushed to his head, the skin on his face tightened and turned a boiling red. "Damn!" He took a couple of deep breaths to compose himself. His mind felt like it was separating from his body. Where was he? Now what? What to do next? In an effort to regroup, he took a deep breath and then gave himself a lecture, "Okay Larry, things will work out. Get it together!" Returning to the business at hand he grabbed his beeper. He had been paged and had calls to return. Whether he wanted to or not, he had to take care of business.

There were three pages. Susan, Red, and Frank Caparelli were all looking for him. Larry took a quick second to call Susan. "Hi there. I got your page."

"Larry, I'm treating you to your favorite meal tonight. Its spaghetti night! Dinner at six okay?"

"Great, that's the first good news of the day."

"I'm sure you'll give me a full report tonight."

"Yes, by then I should have a few things figured out. See ya!"

Larry dialed Red's private line at Town and Country Plumbing. "Hey Red."

"Ratchet, we need to talk. Did you hear about Jimmy?"

"Yes. I just got the bad news."

Red continued, "I'm pretty worked up about it. Can we have breakfast at the Flier's in the morning?"

"Sure, I need to talk to you about something as well"

"Five o'clock as usual?"

"Got it!"

Larry called Frank three times, but his phone was busy. Because Frank was toward the top of the PROH$_2$O food chain, Larry figured he was also having a tough morning. Larry quickly jammed notes, files, and pandemonium into his briefcase. He stuck his head into Brenda's office, thanked her for the use of Jimmy's office, and made plans to head back to his Penny Lane office.

"Your face is beet red. It'll be okay, Larry. Don't get all worked up. Karl is just having a bad day. I already checked with the other branches. Everybody's stock is low on your faucets. I'll work on an order for you. Since I plan on transferring product to other branches that need help, the purchase order should be substantial. Town and Country alone will drain me out of the product on the shelf right now. Give me a few days but you can expect a call from me."

"Thanks, Brenda, I can always count on you to help me out. By the way, there are seven faucets in your bone pile labeled NFG. Unfortunately, I can't accept their return without further information."

"I know that, Larry, it's just that we have a bunch of morons in the warehouse that don't get that. Don't worry about it! I'll take care of it!"

Larry hustled to his van. His head was spinning as he pushed the Astro to its limit down the highway. He muttered to himself, "This feels like a foreign invasion that will change life at the ranch forever!"

Larry turned through the Penny Lane gates and screeched to a halt in front of the barn. The Sarge was grazing in the pasture as Larry entered his unsettled downstairs office. He immediately checked his fax machine. There was yet another fax from PROH$_2$O. As Larry uncoiled the tightly wound memo, his phone rang.

"Connection Sales!"

"Larry, this is Frank, did you see the fax?"

"I got the one from last night, and now I'm unrolling another one."

Larry read the memo aloud slowly, "Effective immediately, Xin Din Industries, operating as PROH$_2$O Faucets, announces a restructuring of the sales department. Frank Caparelli is no longer employed by PROH$_2$O."

Larry stopped reading to catch his breath. "Additionally, manufacturer's reps in the western region previously under Mr. Caparelli's direction are being replaced with a factory direct sales force. Xin Din Industries respectfully thanks the reps involved for their hard work and dedication. This memorandum will serve as the 30 day notification for the affected representatives."

The letter was signed by Hon Do Lee.

"Larry, I know this all sounds horrible..."

Larry was speechless, but not for long. "Horrible? I don't think so. This is devastating!"

"Listen to me Larry. Let me fill you in. I've been very unhappy at PROH$_2$O for quite some time now. The downturn has really hurt their bottom line. I'm sure that's why they sold. In recent months, they cut my expenses, lowered my salary, and raised my quota so high that it became impossible to make a bonus. And then, without consulting with me, new ownership fired my reps! I couldn't believe it! They fired my reps without even knowing anything about them! As you know, my reps are my life blood, they are my friends. When Xin Din terminated them, I had no choice but to resign and get a fresh start. The good news is that I found something very promising and exciting. I just finalized an agreement with a water heater manufacturer. It's a brand new company, called Independence, run by industry people I've known a long time. The part you will love is that I'm in the market for reps."

Larry was silent.

"Larry, are you there?"

"Yes, unfortunately, I am."

"I know you're worried about Connection Sales, but I'm offering you help."

"This feels like an invasion!"

"What?"

"You heard me Frank, in 1968, Igor the Carnivore sent me to the hospital, this morning Karl Tiff shattered my spirit, and now PROH$_2$O is attacking whatever is left of my determination!"

"Larry, you are rambling even crazier than usual. Did you have a stroke or a mental breakdown? I'm trying to help you!"

"I need a bomb shelter!"

"Quit your ridiculous war zone bullshit, you square-headed German and listen to me for once in your life!"

Larry was in a twilight zone moment. His morning flashback to Igor Krakeldorf and the Berry Hill Atom Smashers was locked into his meat locker shaped head with no exit door. He finally replied, "Just let the tanks roll over me and flatten me like Igor did. That will be better than the torture I'm feeling."

"Damn it, Larry, I'm offering you a deal to be my new rep for Independence Water Heater Company."

Larry sat in stark silence.

"Larry, are you there?"

"I'm not sure."

"Did you hear anything I said?"

"I don't know."

"Larry, the water heater business can be very rewarding."

"I thought you said they were a start-up company. Doesn't that mean that their sales in this territory are zero?"

"Well yes, but with your contacts and bull-dogged determination you'll build the territory in no time."

"What's the commission?"

"Don't worry about that now. I'll make sure you're taken care of."

Larry was silent again.

"Larry, talk to me!"

"Well, Frank, even though you didn't tell me what the commission is, I just did the math. I guess it doesn't matter what percentage you are paying. It could be 20% for all I care. The commissionable dollars on zero sales will still be zero. It's pretty hard to pay bills with zero. I've got to think about this. My brain is squashed, my stomach is churning, and I'm just not thinking straight."

Larry hung up the phone and sat in his chair as if he were in a trance. Frank was trying to sell him on hope, but hope alone would not pay the bills. Larry was a clever salesman, but selling Susan on the concept of hope would be tougher than re-gluing the shattered pencil that Karl had deposited on Brenda's desk. Things were plenty tough with the meager commissions $PROH_2O$ was paying, but now Connection Sales was running out of options.

Larry sat dazed, as if he did get steamrolled by a truck or an Igor Krakeldorf. Then he shook his bewildered head just like Sergeant Pepper, and reminded himself he was not a quitter. He just needed to think things through. He needed to devise a plan, a strategy. That was it! He needed to assess and regroup! Red was right! Larry desperately needed a yellow pad and a good sharp pencil. That process needed to start immediately. If he didn't have it all figured out by the time he was having spaghetti with Susan, he would be screwed!

CHAPTER-5

"Bad News Travels Fast"

As Larry stewed about his fractured future, the barnyard office phone rang, sending him back to a fragile reality. "Connection Sales, this is Larry."

"Hello Mr. Larry, this is Hon Do Lee."

"Yes, sir."

"Mr. Larry, I am so sorry that Xin Din Industries has terminated the contracts of their manufacturer's representatives. However, I am calling you to discuss a proposal."

Because the series of events triggered by the stranger had made Larry an emotional wreck, he replied half-heartedly, "Okay."

"Mr. Caparelli has chosen to pursue other interests. However, through my extensive research, I have concluded that you are the perfect choice to be our new western regional sales manager."

"Mr. Lee, you have never met me, but in less than twenty four hours you've fired me and now you are offering to hire me back?"

"Mr. Larry, we did not fire you. We terminated our contract with Connection Sales, as well as the other representative firms in the western region. I am very sorry about the rapid speed of our actions."

"Specifically, what are you offering me?"

"We are prepared to make it worth your while to join our most successful company. Our proposal includes a very aggressive salary, generous reimbursement of expenses and a car of your choosing. Also, Mr. Larry, if you meet our expectations, you will most certainly position yourself for an upper management opportunity."

"Would that be in Cleveland or Shanghai?"

"You have asked a question I am not prepared to answer at this time; however, since we have global interests, the list of opportunities for talented people like you is without end."

"That's a very attractive offer, Mr. Lee. I'll need to discuss it with my wife. Since your original memo of last night, announcing no further changes, just about everything has changed. Will you maintain your operations in Cleveland?"

"To achieve necessary cost reductions, manufacturing will most definitely move to Shanghai, but we believe it is in our best interest to maintain a U.S. position in Cleveland, Ohio. Again, I apologize for the rather rapid reorganization, but Xin Din Industries is a very aggressive company that moves very quickly to insure the success of its many worldwide partners."

"Thank you for your very kind offer, Mr. Lee. I'll need a couple days to make a decision. Please fax me the specifics."

"My secretary will fax it immediately. However, Mr. Larry, a decision by tomorrow would be preferred."

"I have lots to think about. I might need a little more time."

"A prompt reply will be appreciated. Thank you for your consideration of our most generous offer."

Larry was mentally exhausted. He hung up the phone lethargically and sat stunned. Finally, he refocused on the job at hand: a game plan. He needed to jump start his brain by putting a sharp pencil and yellow pad of paper to work, just as Red had reminded him. Larry searched, but failed to locate any pads or pencils in his new office. He unpacked the box he had brought down from his old upstairs office without success.

With the hope that a steaming hot cup of coffee would jump start the thought process, Larry started a fresh pot. He then headed upstairs with an empty box he would re-pack. His heavy steps were slow, and not too sure, but the trails in life are not always traveled easily. Step by step, he finally made it to the top. Larry quickly packed the box, making sure the key ingredients, pads and pencils were in ample supply. He worked his way halfway down the staircase when his phone rang yet again. Four rings later he made it to his desk, set the box down, and grabbed the receiver.

"Connection Sales!"

"This is Brenda! I've been paging you since you left our office. Is it true? PROH$_2$O got sold and fired all their reps?"

"That news traveled to your desk already?"

"So it is true?"

Larry sighed, "Yes, unfortunately it's true."

"Karl told me someone was asking about you."

"Sounds like Hon Do Lee."

"Yeah, that sounds right. Anyway, Karl did give you high marks. He told the man that you were the best rep in the business."

"I find that hard to believe."

"Believe it, Larry. If you think Karl is tough on you, you should see how he treats the other reps. I gave Karl your phone number. He will be calling you."

Larry sighed. "Karl only calls me to rattle my cage!"

Brenda was exasperated. "I don't know, Larry!"

"Thanks for the heads up."

Before Larry could pour coffee into the Ventura beach mug that also served as his security blanket, the phone rang yet again.

"Larry, this is Billy. You were right! Those idiots that work for Mel fried the damn cartridges. And, what's this bullcrap I hear about us losing PROH$_2$O?"

"That news made it all the way to Lancaster?"

"Oh yeah, Mel told me about it."

"How in the world did Mel find out about it? I thought news traveled to Lancaster by pony express."

"The job superintendent for High Desert Builders told him!"

"I would ask you how a superintendent on a dusty job site working out of a job trailer in the middle of nowhere found out something I just learned myself, but that's probably of no use. Well, Billy, sadly it's true. PROH$_2$O was sold and the new owners fired all the reps in the west."

"Holy crap! Now what?"

"Well, we should get paid commissions for everything we sell for the next 30 days, so let's push for all the business we can get."

"10-4 boss."

Larry hung up and paused. As he desperately scrambled to re-set the wheels spinning wildly in his head, the phone rang yet again. "Connection Sales!"

"Larry, this is Karl Tiff."

"Yes sir!"

"You may have heard that Jimmy is no longer with us."

"Yes, I did. What happened?"

"Jimmy drank too much, sold too little and was nothing more than a give-away artist. He came in yesterday at 9:15 with his usual hangover. Because I was just a bit angry, I screamed at him, 'Damn it, Jimmy, don't you know what time we start around here?' Larry, you won't believe his response."

Larry was silent for a moment and then replied, "I don't know Karl. What did Jimmy say?"

"The son of a bitch said, 'How in the hell would I know what time we start. When I get here everyone is already working.'"

"Wow!"

"Wow, just about sums it up. I'm not sure which of us is having a worse day, you or me. Anyway, Larry, I'm sorry for your misfortune with $PROH_2O$. However, as far as I'm concerned, their loss is our gain. We need an injection of new ideas and work ethic. I would like you to go to work for us as our sales manager. It's a big time job with a big time salary plus all the perks. I just sent our offer to you. It's on your fax machine!"

While he continued the conversation, Larry unrolled the faxed offer and quickly looked at it. "That's quite an offer Karl. For your information, $PROH_2O$ also called and offered me a position as western regional sales manager."

"They fired you and then offered you a job?"

"I know. It sounds crazy but that's exactly what happened."

"What did you tell them?"

"I told them it would be hard to abandon a successful rep business, but that I would talk to my wife. I guess I'm telling you the same thing. I need to figure some stuff out. I'm very flattered. Can I have a day or two to decide?"

"Of course, Larry, I understand."

Larry put the phone down, still in shock. He stood up from his chair to get that cup of coffee he was so desperate for, but the trail of calls was unrelenting.

"Connection Sales!"

"This is Emily. Remember me, I work for you? Oh my goodness! Please tell me it isn't true. Please!"

"Sorry to say it is true."

"Well Larry, don't you think it would have been nice for you to let me know? Here I am in Santa Maria when a counterman tells me about it. Don't you think that hurts?"

"I'm so sorry. I haven't been able to call anyone because the phone is ringing nonstop. How in the world did the counterman find out?"

"From the competition! I just can't believe the rep from Alpha found out before I did. Sometimes I wonder to myself why I'm in this business. You and I both worked for the factory before they decided to go with reps, and now that we are reps, they decide they want to go back to factory sales people. What in the world is wrong with these people? Are we going to be okay?"

"Honestly, I don't know. I'm ready to unplug my phone so I can think."

"I'm really sorry, Larry."

"Me too, Emily."

Larry's phone had turned into a loaded gun, ready to go off any second.

"Connection Sales."

"Ratchet! What's this horse shit I just heard? I can kind of understand Jimmy losing his job. The son of a bitch is always drunk. But you? I really can't believe it! How in the hell could those people do this to you? Those sons of bitches will pay for this. Mark my words. I'm done buying their faucets!"

"It's been quite a day, Red."

"Sorry for the tirade, Ratchet, but I need a damn tractor to scoop up the avalanche of manure landing on my trail. Keep the faith. Let's eat at Sal's instead of the Fliers. Breakfast here in town makes more sense because I have a meeting with a builder in San Diego at nine o'clock."

"You can tell them that you'll be providing Independence Water Heaters on the next job."

"You never cease to amaze me Ratchet. You really are going to make me crazy!"

"See ya' at five!"

Larry unplugged the phone and finally took a sip of coffee, but it was cold; a bitter cold that summed up the day! When expectations are high and results are low, even the *Jelly Beans in Life* can be put to the test. After a few soul searching moments, Larry shook himself and committed himself to pressing forward. He settled into his chair and held his pencil firmly in his hand. A blank yellow pad eagerly awaited restoration to sanity. Larry drifted into a spaced out, mind traveling daze that felt like ten seconds but in reality lasted thirty minutes.

"Larry!"

There was no response.

"LARRY!"

Larry was startled. He looked up to find Susan standing directly in front of him. She was holding back tears. "Why am I always the last one to know anything?"

"What?"

"You know exactly what I'm talking about! I suppose you didn't get my page?"

"Yes, I did. Remember, I called you."

"Larry! That was this morning! I've paged you six times since then!"

Larry looked at his pager in dismay.

Susan continued, "Then I called your office number to find it is out of service."

"Oh, I just unplugged it."

"Nicely done, Larry! So I walk down Penny Lane and see your Astro. Now I'm worried sick. I walk in, and there you are with a blank look and a blank yellow pad in front of you. Your bewildered expression stopped me in my tracks. Then I see you holding a sharp pencil in one hand and grasping your coffee mug with the other. What were you thinking about doing, stabbing yourself to death?"

Larry deeply inhaled and slowly exhaled.

"It's been a brutal day."

"I know all about it."

"You do?"

Susan was losing patience. "Of course I do! Even though you tried to hide critical information from me, I found out anyway!"

"What did you find out?"

"That PROH$_2$O terminated your contract."

"Susan, I was going to tell you over dinner. I unplugged the phone because it just wouldn't stop ringing. I was trying to figure stuff out. Maybe I'm traveling along a trail headed to the funny farm. How did you find out?"

"Mayor Sam called me."

Larry was puzzled. "How did he find out?"

"From Sal at the diner!"

Larry was getting frustrated. "Holy crap. How did he find out?"

"From Mary!"

Larry put two and two together. "I get it. Mary found out from Red."

"Exactly! So you told Red before you bothered to tell me."

Larry shook his head and heaved a big sigh. "Actually, that's not true. I know that Red knows because he told me he knows, but I didn't tell him."

Now Susan's anger amplified into a scream, "What?"

Larry replied with a truth that, at that moment, was impossible for Susan to believe, "I haven't told anyone, but somehow everybody knows everything about everything and I don't have a clue about anything."

CHAPTER 6

"Spaghetti"

Susan was speechless. That was bad. Real bad! A quietly stewing Susan was never good. She turned her head to one side as if changing the angle of the eye contact would add perspective. Larry and Susan held their positions silently for seconds that felt like minutes. Because his emotions were about to explode, Larry broke the tense moment with a forced smile and a deep breath. He looked at his watch. It was now 4:15. Somehow, four hours had fast forwarded since he first read the fax that terminated Connection Sales and sent him into a deep Ventura fog. He finally initiated an awkward attempt to jump-start communication, "So Susan, are we still having spaghetti at six?"

Again silence.

Larry continued, "I hadn't really thought about it, but I haven't eaten anything all day."

No response! Nothing!

Larry made another attempt to move the ball forward, "Your spaghetti is absolutely amazing!"

Susan was still steaming, "Really? That's it? That's all you've got to say?"

Susan shook her head, abruptly turned, and walked away. One step from the barn door she turned her head and mumbled a reply to a paralyzed Larry, "I'm having spaghetti at six. It seems to me that you've declared your independence and that you're going to do whatever the heck you want, regardless of what I think or say."

Larry's voice projected up the driveway at a briskly walking Susan, "You know I love your spaghetti!"

Susan was heading up Penny Lane to the simmering sauce that she had prepared earlier. It was unclear which liquid was bubbling at a higher temperature, the sizzling marinara in the pan on the stove or the boiling blood in her veins. Larry's weak effort to make peace had failed. Susan was angry, scared, and hurt because information that had the potential to destroy her life at the ranch with Larry was discovered third hand. Ideally, at that precise moment, Larry would have put his sharp pencil to work on the inviting yellow pad, but in life and business, urgency trumps priority and actions demand reactions. Susan had acted and he needed to react.

Armed with his pencil and pad, Larry made his way up Penny Lane. As he reached the top of the steep incline, Charlie greeted him as if he had just returned from two weeks out of the country. Larry patted him on the head. Charlie licked Larry's hand as if to say everything would be fine. As usual, the steep driveway sucked the wind out of Larry's lungs. Before going into the house to make peace with Susan, he took a seat on the deck to harness all the mental and physical energy he could muster up. Remarkably, even though he was out of breath, trampled remnants of resolve re-surfaced. The view of the lake, in that split second, was nothing short of majestic; majesty that added a sprinkle of peace into a stormy afternoon.

Susan's supportive voice startled Larry. "Maybe a glass of wine will help."

Larry wore a bewildered smile as he accepted Susan's peace offering. "I've spent the whole day being blindsided by a chain of events that has me feeling like I'm the lead vehicle in an eighteen car pile-up. But you? You have a knack for knowing what I need. You are the doctor with the right medicine. The magician that pulls a rabbit out of her hat at precisely the right moment. Thanks."

Susan gently seated herself on the patio chair next to Larry, delicately holding her wine glass, and viewing the spectrum of a crazy day through the moist prisms of her eyes.

"Susan, I know I'm a pig headed romantic that from time to time loses sight of reality. And yes, I do cherish working as an independent rep, but I never, ever want to be independent of you."

"Does that mean that you are finally going to tell me how independent Larry's business fell apart today?"

"Well, it all started with the 'Pencil Breaker' ripping my hard earned purchase order to shreds. Then it got worse. PROH$_2$O was sold to a Chinese company who said they would change nothing, but in the time it took you to cook spaghetti, they changed everything. Frank was gone and so was I! Then it got even crazier because the new owner that fired me offered to hire me back to replace Frank. A phone call later, the guy that ripped up the order I was supposed to get, offered me a job to replace my friend Jimmy, who was fired. Then in the midst of the turmoil, Frank, who took a job as sales manager for a company called Independence Water Heaters, offered me a contract to represent a line of products with no income but car loads of hope."

"I'm in no mood to hear storyteller Larry tell me a fable. Please save those stories for Charlie and Sergeant Pepper."

Larry took a huge breath of ranch air and then proceeded to tell the entire story to Susan, who sat in confused disbelief. "Larry, please don't make me move from the ranch."

"If I take the job with Xin Din Industries, we would definitely be packing boxes."

"Frank operates out of his house."

"But that was before. Unfortunately, this is now. If I accept the position and do a great job, we will end up moving to Cleveland or Shanghai. If I do a bad job, I'll be fired. Neither trail will keep us on Penny Lane, or lead us to any place we would ever want to go."

Susan dissected the fragments of verbal horse manure Larry had placed before her. "Okay, Larry, forget about Xin Din Industries' offer. But just because Karl Tiff shattered your pencil and ripped up your order, it doesn't mean you couldn't work for him and be happy. Everybody knows that Jimmy drinks too much, so you can't blame Karl for firing him."

"I understand, but taking that job just seems like a step backwards."

"No, Larry! Losing the ranch would be going backwards! Don't tell me you're thinking about keeping Connection Sales alive?"

"I don't know. I really don't know. I was hoping my sharp pencil and yellow pad would fuel clarity."

"Larry, you're barely breaking even now. What makes you think that losing faucet commissions and replacing them with hope will pay the bills? The last time I checked, the bank is not accepting deposits of hope."

Larry sat still. The yellow pad was still blank. The pencil was still sharp.

Susan continued, "I'll be right back. I need to check on the spaghetti."

Opportunity fueled inspiration. Larry's mind immediately began noodling. His sharp pencil started working its magic, much like a primitive computer. He wrote down the plusses and minuses of all three opportunities. Opportunity! That was the key word. It really wasn't a bad day after all. He had three great opportunities to explore. The key was to make the best choice for today and tomorrow. The choice to stay a manufacturer's rep had few short term plusses and many question marks. It was difficult to determine if those questions would be answered with plusses or minuses. He did some quick math. If Connection Sales had no employees, could he make a go of it? How about his employees? What would become of them? Larry hoped they would be hired back by PROH$_2$O as factory salesmen.

Without commissions from PROH$_2$O, the only money coming in would be from six small lines that would cover his business expense but offer himself no salary. There were many days when Larry considered the small factories with small commissions to be more trouble than they were worth. If he stayed the course and stayed in the rep business, they might be his life line. The financial shape of Connection Sales had become very fragile, but a very successful first year in 1987 had put money in the bank. That money was still there. Those reserves could be used as a safety net. That safety net would be small, but nonetheless could help smooth out a sporadic cash flow position.

"The spaghetti will be ready in five minutes."

Larry didn't hear Susan's announcement. He was mesmerized by the notes, scribbles, and calculations that filled the yellow pad.

"Larry!"

"Oh, I'm sorry. I guess I was in my own little world."

"In your own little world? As usual, you were traveling across the universe in your own space capsule."

Larry got up, clutching his cherished pad and pencil. After a sip of wine he set his life navigation tools on the patio table and walked into the kitchen. "It looks like you have things under control. You need to teach me that art. It seems like I'm always spinning out of control."

"Dinner is just about ready. Please feed Charlie. I'll fix our plates."

Larry wrapped Charlie's pills in a slice of American cheese and dropped it onto the two scoops of senior dog food that was poured into a Charlie-sized bowl. "I know you would rather have spaghetti, but maybe there'll be some leftovers."

A refreshing evening breeze welcomed Larry as he sat down next to Susan. Since the Schafers had not resolved the issue at hand, there was no clicking of wine glasses. Larry took a bite. "Well, you did it again! Tastes like you added a secret ingredient to the sauce."

"You're very perceptive. Yes I did."

"What was it?"

"If I told you it would no longer be a secret, would it? It seems that you don't share your secrets with me, so I'm taking your lead. So what is independent Larry thinking?"

"It's a secret."

That response triggered a very aggravated Susan look.

Larry scrambled to get the conversation back on track. "I'm just kidding. Well, I still need to let my ideas simmer a bit, but I think I might be heading down a trail that will provide answers."

"I'm listening."

Larry continued, "Well, it's still a little half-baked. I only had nine minutes to put my sharp pencil to work."

"Are you going to put your plan back in the oven, or are you going to share it with me?"

"This has been a really crazy day. Please believe me when I tell you that it was never my intent to keep you in the dark."

Susan held back tears and simply replied, "Okay."

Larry moved forward with his loosely thought out plan "You and I agree that we want no part of Xin Din Industries' proposal, correct?"

"That's correct."

"That leaves us two proposals: the 'shattered pencil' offer by Karl Tiff and the 'car load of hope' proposition by Frank."

Susan took a bite of spaghetti and a sip of wine. Charlie plopped down in the corner, adjacent to the negotiating table.

Larry plowed ahead. "The 'shattered pencil' program would definitely pay the bills, but I would lose the independence of being a rep. I really want to explore the water heater program. I need to talk to Red and a few other trusted friends."

"How about me, Larry, are you going to talk to me?"

Larry searched to find thoughts that could be converted into a compelling argument, words that would have even a slight chance of making sense. "Connection Sales might be viable if I had no employees and a little help from the water heater people."

"How in the world would you cover all that territory by yourself?"

"By planning my work and working my plan!"

"That sounds like another Larry fable that you should tell to Sergeant Pepper. Even Charlie would not believe that fairy tale. There is no way on God's green earth that you are going to cover half of the state of California on your own, trying to sell an unknown brand to people you don't even know! I'm sure Red will help you. He always does. But how many friends do you have in Bakersfield, Chula Vista, or Van Nuys?"

"I'll only need to do it for about a year. After that, I should be able to add reinforcements."

"So you will convert hope to cash and maintain your independence?"

"Exactly!"

"And, I suppose you'll live in your tired old Astro van and drive it 100,000 miles a year?"

"I would if that's what it takes!"

"Larry, surely you don't believe that. The graph lines on your yellow pad do not intersect. Hope and independence, in this case, are rays heading in opposite directions. If hope resides in San Diego and independence is located in Paso Robles, how in the world are you going to connect the two from Lake Mathias? I know you consider yourself the king of connecting dots, but I'm beginning to think that the dots in your life are headed down one trail while you're traveling up another one."

Charlie was frustrated. Larry and Susan were so busy fighting for and against independence that they had forgotten he even existed. Would all the leftovers find their way into a container, locked in the refrigerator?

CHAPTER 7

"Common Sense at Sal's"

The next morning, Larry made a very quick stop in his office. A handful of faxes awaited his arrival; nothing urgent from PROH$_2$O, Karl Tiff, or Frank, though. Four small orders for his other lines were forwarded efficiently. He was surprised to see he had no messages on his answer machine, but quickly remembered he had unplugged his phone. As he reconnected it, he hoped that the result would not be yet another avalanche of calls. Time was ever so precious. It was 4:20 AM. Breakfast with Red was at 5:00. Larry started the coffee maker and opened the Dutch door. The well-orchestrated ritual culminated with his coffee mug filling and the Sarge receiving a handful of jelly beans.

Coffee bean energizers flavored the air as Larry again used Sergeant Pepper as a sounding board. "Good morning, Sarge. Susan told me that going into the water heater business and keeping Connection Sales alive is proof that I believe the Easter bunny actually does hide eggs in the garden. She believes only you would be interested in listening to me talk about my crazy idea of remaining an independent businessman. She insists I'm a dreamer. I think she's a pessimist, but she says she's merely a realist. I think by the end of today, I'll know what is real and what is not. My mission today is to connect dots and draw a clear line between common sense and nonsense. Yes, today is a really big day. Take it easy big fellow. I'll talk to you tonight or tomorrow."

As Larry eased through the Penny Lane gate, he took a reassuring sip of hot brew. In his mind, the Astro was transformed into the Woodie that decorated his coffee cup. Dry desert air was replaced with a sea breeze. He shook himself and awakened from the daydream. Perhaps Susan was right. Perhaps his mind had slipped into a fantasy land. Was his swirling mind just tired or was he going crazy?

After a short drive through dark country roads, Larry arrived at Sal's Café. He walked across a lonely parking lot and steadied himself. It was time to get down to business. As he walked through the front door of the tiny restaurant, he was immediately reminded that bad news travels fast. Sal immediately asked, "So what's it gonna be Larry? Are you going into the water heater business, moving to Shanghai, or taking Jimmy's job while back ordering the whiskey?"

To fuel his role as 'the informer', Sal needed the inside scoop. His café was a front for information gathering. His keen ears heard every detail of every conversation in his restaurant. After processing the data, he spun rumors to his liking and spread them around town, one customer at a time. Larry had just taken his first step into Sal's and already regretted it. He chose a table in the corner. "Hi Sal, I'll take this table because it's furthest away from your big ears."

"Don't forget, there is no better coffee in the world than what you get right here from your buddy Sal." Larry was certain that his barn coffee was better than Sal's, but he was in no mood for a coffee debate with Sal the morning after the war of independence with Susan.

Right on cue, Red walked in and sat down as Sal returned with coffees in hand. "What do you think, Red? It sounds like our friend Larry is overloaded with choices."

Red smiled. He always smiled. He smiled even when Sal, Larry, or one of his plumbers irritated him. "Sal, I'll go with the usual."

"The same for you, Larry?"

"Please!"

Sal chuckled. "Thanks for keeping things lively, Larry. If folks around town weren't talking about you, they'd be at a loss for words."

Larry remarked sarcastically, "Any idea where my neighbors are discovering news about me that Susan doesn't even know?"

Sal ignored the question. "Your breakfast will be coming right up, gentlemen!"

Red took a sip of Sal's coffee and asked Larry, "Are you thinking about taking Jimmy's job?"

"I will if I have to. Red, if I went into the water heater business, would you support me?"

"I've told you before that I'd support you on just about anything you "got your hands on, provided it makes even a little bit of sense."

"Do you think my going into the water heater business makes even a little bit of sense?"

"So you did some noodling with your sharp pencil and came up with this nonsense?"

"Water heaters have become my first choice."

"Well, Ratchet, are you going to sell them to me directly?"

"You know I can't do that, Red. Selling direct to contractors is rep suicide."

"Since nobody stocks this new line of water heaters, how in the hell will I get them?"

"Well, if you'll allow me to tell distributors that you'll be buying my heaters, I'll get a wholesaler in short order."

"How about pricing? How can I commit to something without pricing?"

"I'm hoping that you'll trust me when I say that the price will be right."

"The school I went to taught me that a water heater is a water heater. But what if these new heaters are a piece of crap? Screw-ups hit me in the wallet, big time! Today's tight contracts have no wiggle room for problems."

"I don't know, Red, but I'll find out. I would never sell a product I don't believe in myself!"

"So you have no distributors, no pricing, and you're not sure if these damn things are any good. How in the hell can I commit to that? It would make no sense whatsoever to commit to a program that is filled with bullshit!"

Sal returned with crispy bacon and eggs over medium with biscuits soaked in greasy gravy. "Anything else, fellows?"

"Thanks, Sal. Looks good!"

"I really appreciate your support on this, Red; it means a lot to me."

"Ratchet, I didn't say I was supporting this nonsense."

"I know. But I think just maybe you will."

"So who else are you going to hit up with this half-baked idea?"

"Well, I have a short list, but I think I'll be able to figure stuff out once I talk to everyone. After I meet with Brenda at Sunnymeade Pipe and Supply, I'm either driving to Ventura to pick the brains of my friends up there, or heading to L.A. to soak in Clarence Silverman's wisdom."

"So, are these water heater people from out of the country?"

"Absolutely not! Independence Water Heaters is owned by Americans and manufactured in America."

"I suppose you'll be selling them to hardware stores as well?"

"No. These water heaters are engineered for licensed contractors and will be sold only through wholesale distributors."

"That's the first thing you've said all morning that makes any sense at all. Don't you think that the quality will be good if they're engineered for plumbers?"

"Red, you said that, not me. But I do agree with you. I just haven't seen any yet or heard that much about them."

"Ratchet, I don't suppose it's cheap to start up a water heater factory. So my guess is that they do a good job of making them. If they make bad product, they'll quickly go out of business and lose their investment. That would be bad business. What does Frank say about these water heater people?"

"Frank says they have a long history in the business and are very honorable."

"Well there you go, Ratchet, what are you worried about?"

"So now you're telling me that this DOES make sense?"

"Maybe. But you gotta get me good prices and a distributor."

"I sure wish Susan was as easy to sell on this idea as you. She pretty much thinks I've lost my marbles for even thinking about staying the course with Connection Sales."

"Sorry, Ratchet, but that's your battle to fight. From where I sit, things that make common sense to men can be absolute bullshit to women!"

The two friends finished their breakfast and received to-go cups for their road trips. On Larry's cup, Sal wrote with a black marker the words,

"GOOD LUCK". Larry knew that, even though he and Red were seated in the far corner, Sal had heard every word.

While Red was headed to San Diego, Larry used the pay phone in the parking lot to make credit card calls to Brenda, Big Ben, and Steve to schedule appointments. Intent on having heart to heart conversations with Emily and Billy, he left messages on the answer machines of his employees. He checked his beeper and was relieved there were no pages. Larry poured Sal's coffee from its Styrofoam container into his Ventura mug of dreams. As he drove, he added Frank to the list of calls he needed to make on his fact finding mission. Next stop: Sunnymeade Pipe and Supply.

"Hi Brenda!"

"Larry, I just about have that order put together. Will you be getting commission on it?"

"Thanks, Brenda. Yes, legally $PROH_2O$ must pay me commission for 30 days. Where did you find a purchase order you could write up?"

"I'm sure you know the answer to that question. I'll be sure to fatten it up so that your last check from them will be a bit larger."

"You are far too kind. But, don't get yourself in trouble with Karl. I don't want him breaking anymore of your pencils."

"Not to worry, Larry. I keep a good-sized inventory of pencils in my hiding place as well."

"So, Brenda, Karl offered me Jimmy's job."

"That's great!"

"Not so quick, kiddo. I told him I would let him know by tomorrow, but my goal is to stay in the rep business. I have an opportunity to be the rep for a new water heater company called Independence. How difficult would it be for me to get my water heaters into your branches?"

"Oh boy, Larry. That's a really tough one. Since you've never been in the water heater business, let me caution you. Switching water heater lines would be a really big deal for us. Distributors are known in the market for their fixture and water heater alignment. I'm not saying it couldn't happen, but don't expect anything quickly. Job one, of course would be plumber support."

"Red is ready to buy them."

"Red's ready to buy something you haven't even committed to?"

"We had breakfast this morning. First he thought the whole idea of me going into the water heater business was ridiculous. Then he kind of changed his mind and said he'd support me if I headed down that trail."

"You don't waste any time, do you? Well, that's a start, but only a start. What does Susan have to say about this?"

"She pretty much thinks I would be foolish not to take Karl's offer. We do both agree that going to work at Xin Din Industries would be a mistake."

"Larry, the water heater business isn't easy. But, if anyone can make a go of it, you're probably the guy. However, I doubt you will be able to get a major distributor to stock your product. I would love to help you, but Karl and his bosses make decisions on water heaters. My advice to you: don't piss off Susan or Karl!"

"Thanks Brenda. You've managed to add confusion to my dilemma of separating common sense and nonsense."

"Don't be such a hardhead, Larry. You DO need to use some common sense. If you really want to sell water heaters, sell them here working for us. Your office will be right next to mine. How bad would that be?"

"Okay, Brenda, I get it, but I just hate to throw away my career as an independent rep. With your help, I suppose I could handle Jimmy's job, but I'm just not sure that I'm cut out for the corporate life."

"You'll be fine, Larry. Karl doesn't wear a tie, and you won't have to either."

"I'm not positive, but it kind of sounds like you're taking Susan's side."

"I'm not taking Susan's side. I'm taking Karl's side and my side. Do you have any idea how much I hate doing both my job and Jimmy's?"

"Okay, I understand. The problem is that I'm being tugged in lots of directions. No matter what I decide, somebody will be disappointed. Any chance I can use Jimmy's office to make a couple of calls?"

"You know the answer to that. Spend all the time you want in there.

Maybe you'll take a liking to it."

Larry went into Jimmy's office and went right to work. The first order of business was to call Frank.

"Good morning!"

"Larry, how in the hell are you doing. Thanks for calling me back. I've got really great news for you."

Larry looked at his pager. There it was: the page from Frank. "I'm still sorting things out, Frank, so I don't have an answer yet."

"Let me throw a little weight on our offer and make the decision a bit easier for you. We are certainly not underestimating the magnitude of the challenge ahead of you, so we're going to give you a helping hand. I know your Astro is on its last legs. Since I can't afford to have my star rep stranded on a highway, broken down in the middle of nowhere, I convinced management to provide you with a brand new Dodge Caravan."

Larry was stunned and for a moment speechless. "Larry, are you there?"

"Holly shit, Frank! That's very generous. I'm overwhelmed. But, just out of curiosity, why would you get me a Caravan? You know I'm an Astro guy."

"If you'd rather have an Astro, I can make that happen. But I've been watching you climb into your van, and it's not pretty. I went to the Chevy and Dodge dealerships last night. The Caravan is a lot lower to the ground. I'm certain that you'll find it easier to get in and out of and a lot more comfortable. Plus, it doesn't have that big hump in the middle, so you'll have considerably more room to spread out your legs. To get this program going, you'll be on the road a lot. I'm pretty sure that when you're driving to Santa Maria, you'll thank me for the comfort the Caravan gives you."

"I feel like a kid on Christmas morning! You really did your homework! Everything you said makes perfectly good sense. I'm unbelievably lucky to have a friend like you!"

"Didn't I tell you that I was going to take care of you?"

"Well, yes you did."

"Larry, I've got one more thing. It seems to me that you're not too good at minding your pager. And then, when you finally do get a page you've got to find a phone. Because we can't afford to have you operate inefficiently, we're going to supply you with a mobile phone and the reasonable monthly charges."

Larry was quiet again.

"For God sakes, Larry, are you there."

"You're making it really hard for me to say no."

"Then say yes!"

Larry ignored Frank's attempt to close the deal. "How about the commission, do you have that worked out?"

"It is worked out. I have it right here. Are you near a fax machine?"

"There's one right here in Jimmy's old office. I'm at Sunnymeade Pipe and Supply. By the way, it doesn't sound like they're going to buy Independence Water Heaters any time soon."

After giving Frank the fax number, Larry watched the rolled memo slowly jitter through. "Okay, Frank, I've got it right here. From the looks of it, I need to learn to sell commercial water heaters. You guys pay big dollars on those. The residential water heater commission is considerably less generous."

"Thirties, forties and fifties are a volume business. You'll need to find volume buyers."

"That will be tough in the midst of a housing crash."

"Larry, the water heater business is a replacement business. That's where you need to spend your time. New work housing is the frosting on the cake, but not the meat and potatoes. You're smart, you'll find a balance. Just use all your resources."

"Frank, how did you learn so much about the water heater business overnight?"

"I started my career in the water heater business. The faucet business was just a convenient interruption."

"Well, I guess I'm playing catch-up, although I sold plenty of water heaters at Dick's, and installed a bunch of them with Big Ben. Red's already on board, but I need to find a wholesaler to carry inventory."

"That a boy Larry. You can do this. I just know you can. Just remember that the L.A. market will be the key. That's definitely water heater country. Get yourself into the San Fernando Valley. The hundreds of apartment complexes built in the fifties all have commercial water heaters. Do the math and you'll see that it adds up to a very large number! The millions of people living in the L.A. market all need hot water. There's indisputable power in large numbers. Think about that Larry! It's a beautiful thing!"

"I think I get it."

"So Larry, are you ready to start?"

"Well, not quite. I was heading to Ventura to talk to Steve at Dick's and Big Ben, but that plan might need to be scrapped. Based on the conversation I just had with Brenda, I also need to talk to RP Supply in Riverside. As I learn a little bit about the water heater business, some of the stuff I thought would make sense just doesn't make sense anymore. Separating sense and nonsense is making my head hurt. I need to rethink my plans for the day before I spin my wheels on a bad plan."

"Larry, here's rule number one in the water heater business. Whenever something just doesn't make sense, refer to this rule."

"Alright Frank, what is it?"

"Never apply logic to the water heater business."

Larry's mind was fried. He hung up the phone in a daze and made his way to Brenda's office. While he was in Jimmy's office talking to Frank, Brenda had been rehearsing her sales pitch to Larry. "If that chair isn't comfortable enough, we'll get you a new one. I'm certain Karl will do whatever it takes to get you into that office as our sales manager. Working for a stable company like ours makes good common sense."

Larry shook his head and replied, "Have you been talking to Susan?"

"No, but it's beginning to sound like I need to!"

CHAPTER 8

"The Tijuana Brass"

Larry drove down the highway struggling to find some sense of sanity. His plan! What in the world happened to his plan? What was the plan anyway? Would it work? Would it lead him to make a decision by tomorrow morning? He needed to make a decision in 24 hours but he had a myriad of dots to connect. He shook himself. Job one was to find an Independence distributor who would sell water heaters to Red. If Larry did that, would he be confident enough to go forward with Frank? After all, Frank said that the replacement market was the key. L.A. was the key. Commercial water heaters in the valley were a huge opportunity. How could Larry research the market for Independent Water Heaters in L.A. in 24 hours?

He still needed to talk with Emily and Billy for the purpose of getting them off his payroll and onto PROH$_2$O's. Only a few un-connected dots ago, Larry had three employees. Now, provided Connection Sales was a viable entity, he would be going it alone.

Ventura? Perhaps that plan would be scrapped for the day. Maybe he should he go back to his office and gather information on the phone instead of driving down congested freeways searching for dot interchanges. But if he went back to his office, would the phone's constant ringing prevent him from calling the friends and associates he actually needed to talk to?

Those darn dots! There were just so many to connect. What about Frank? Wasn't he a loyal, considerate friend? And Brenda! It was amazing to see how much she wanted Larry to work in the office next to hers. What should Larry plunge into, the wholesale business or the water heater business? The truth was, he really didn't know much about either one. The one thing he knew about was the faucet business, but that had turned sour.

And Susan! Yes Susan! He still needed to connect the biggest dots of all. The dots that separated he and his wife. After parking the Astro, Larry rifled through his briefcase. A yellow pad and pencil! Where were they? On his desk on Penny Lane! Damn! Since the probability of connecting all those dots without a yellow pad and sharp pencil was zero, a return to his office had suddenly become a must. He did have his Franklin Planner, but in times of crises he always reverted back to the 8½ x 11 writing tablets.

As Larry climbed out of the van, he thought about how unprepared he was to talk to Russ Petersen, the president of RP Supply. Frank had just given Larry a ten minute overview on the water heater business, no doubt a good start to his education. But serious meetings, like the one he was about to have with Mr. P, would require much more substance. Nonetheless, he would do the best he could with the tools he had. After all, this was a fact-finding mission, nothing more.

Russ was a large man, but his physical being paled in comparison with his commanding presence. Any rep or employee that ever walked into Russ Petersen's office understood the critical importance of having smart answers for the smart questions that would be forthcoming. Larry was equipped with one set of tools that could give him a fighting chance; he was confident without being cocky.

As he walked through the front door, Larry was immediately greeted by Jimmy, Karl Tiff's former sales manager and Red's longtime wholesale "go-to" guy; the Jimmy who had been in the business most of his fifty-nine years on earth and coped best after a shot of whiskey. His personality did not match his tightly curled Shirley Temple hair, but plumbers like Red associated well with him because he knew his stuff and was one of the good old boys. It also helped that he was a salesman who consistently under-cut his competitors.

"What the heck are you doing here, Jimmy?"

"I just interviewed with Mr. Petersen, and he hired me. I have a job provided I clean up my act and deliver some of Red's business."

Larry gave Jimmy a high five. "That's great!"

"I heard about your faucet people. So what are your plans? You're not thinking about going to work as PROH$_2$O's sales manager, are you?"

"No, not really! I'm thinking about going into the water heater business."

Jimmy was surprised. "You're kidding, right? What do you know about water heaters?"

"Very little!"

"What water heater brand?"

"Independence."

"Never heard of them! They must be new."

"Correct!"

"You should talk to Red about them."

"Already done! He's on board."

"Larry, you gave Red prices?"

"No."

"Did you give him a rebate?"

"No."

"Then how in the hell did you sell him on these water heaters?"

"Well, I really didn't. He kind of sold himself on the idea and then sold me on it."

"What?"

"I don't know Jimmy, but that's how it went down."

"You need to talk to Mr. P."

"That's exactly why I'm here."

"Great! Get them in here and I'll sell the crap out of them for you! Make sure you give us some hot prices."

"I haven't even agreed to be the rep for Independence and I have no pricing information. The fact of the matter is, I really don't know that much about water heaters."

"Here's all you need to know, Larry. They gotta have a five year warranty, they gotta be cheap, and when you order a truckload of 150, you gotta discount them three dollars. They call that an unloading allowance."

Larry was incredulous. "Water heater companies pay customers to unload trucks?"

"Yes! Can you believe it?"

"That doesn't make any sense. The faucet people sure as heck don't do that."

Larry stopped himself. He was beginning to understand what Frank said. He immediately reverted to rule number one: never apply logic to the water heater business!

As he shook Jimmy's hand, his pager started to go crazy. Emily and Billy were both looking for him. Oops, and so was Susan. Beep…and now PROH$_2$O. Larry guessed it was Hon Do Lee. All of that would have to wait. He really needed to talk to Mr. Petersen about a subject he seemed to know the least about: water heaters. Larry turned and made his way to Marsha's desk offering nothing more than a forced smile.

"Larry, you look like all the screws in your head just came loose."

"Hello, Marsha, I'm here to see Mr. Petersen."

"Are you sure? You might think about getting some work done under your hood before you see Mr. P."

The thing Marsha liked best about her job was acting as the gatekeeper, teasing the salesmen who were desperate to have a meeting with her boss. She relished the sight of businessmen squirming for a hall pass to the classroom of the no-nonsense plumbing guru, Russ Petersen.

Marsha picked the phone up and rang the president of RP Supply. "Larry from Connection Sales is here to see you."

She turned back to Larry. "You got the green light. Good luck."

In Southern California, there were no single location plumbing wholesalers that did more volume than RP Supply. Because Russ's wife also worked in the business, he enjoyed referring to his company as just a little ma and pa business. Manufacturers and reps knew better. When Mr. P committed to distributing a product, RP Supply delivered impressive sales numbers that rivaled those of much larger companies. He loved to take an order off the street by aggressively packaging an offer while his competition was still devising a sales strategy.

Russ was protective of a relatively short list of customers who were very reluctant to cross Mr. P by purchasing from his competitors. He was well renowned for having absolute control of his business and customers.

Mr. P was also famous for taking money from an unsuspecting rep or a factory man on the golf course. Russ' golf swing and business approach were unorthodox, but both were superbly effective. The thing Larry liked best about Mr. P was his way of simplifying business, making it easy to do one hour of business in five minutes. Larry had other customers who milked two hours of his time to do five minutes of business.

Larry walked down the long hallway to an office the size of a luxury apartment. It featured a private restroom, bar, and wrap-around sofa. A private back door led to a garage that housed classic cars.

"Hello Mr. P, how goes it?"

"Just fine, Larry. To what do I owe this visit?"

"I wanted to congratulate you on hiring Jimmy."

"I'm hoping for the best. Jimmy and I have agreed on some ground rules. He has lots of plusses. What I like best about him is that plumbing contractors love him. So what's this I hear about your misfortune with $PROH_2O$?"

"Yes, I'm afraid it's true. They've terminated all of their western reps, replacing them with factory people. They offered me a position as a western regional sales manager, but I'm leaning towards staying in the rep business. Frank Caparelli is now working for a water heater company called Independence and offered me the line."

"Larry, what do you know about the water heater business?"

"Well, not much."

"Let me help you out. Whereas all distributors carry the same faucet lines, small companies, like ours, only inventory one brand of water heaters. If you become the rep for Independence, the first thing you need to understand is that for you to get your product into my warehouse, you would need to replace Copper Tank, my current supplier. I do not and will not stock two brands. The investment is too large and the space required is too great."

"Thank you, Mr. P, I know I have lots to learn. I did have breakfast with my friend, Red. If, indeed, I do go into the water heater business, Red will support me and move his business to Independence."

"That's a good start, Larry. It sounds like all you need is a distributor. Unfortunately for you, it won't be me. I'm very loyal to my current supplier. The only way you would ever have an opportunity to sell me water heaters is for my friends at Copper Tank to have a problem supplying me product."

"I get it. Sounds like Independence would be on the outside looking in for a long, long time."

"Don't be so sure, Larry. The water heater business is full of surprises."

"That's what I hear. Thank you very much for the valuable lesson."

"Stay light on your feet! You just never know when opportunity will knock on your door."

As Larry walked down the long hall, it was unclear if the visit with Mr. P helped Larry connect dots or made the task more difficult.

Upon returning to the reception area, Marsha had a suspicious look, "Well Larry, I'm not sure if the loose screws in your head are loosening or tightening. Mr. P is a pretty good mechanic. Did he open the hood and take a look inside?"

"Actually, I think he did, but I'm not sure I liked the diagnosis. Would it be okay to use the phone on the counter?"

"Larry, don't act like a stranger! You know you can use that phone anytime you want."

Larry smiled and worked his way to a crowded will-call area filled with activity. He parked himself at the end of the counter in front of a phone and called Emily. "Hi, what's up?"

Emily tried to speak but her sobbing prevented it. She finally mustered up the only words she could squeeze out of her mouth, "I'm so sorry!"

Now Larry was shaken. "Are you okay?"

"Yes...but no."

"Oh my, I don't know what to say."

Emily gathered herself, finally able to communicate her feelings. "I've been sitting here fussing and fretting, just waiting for you to call me back."

Larry turned his back to the activity at the will-call counter to create some sense of privacy, "It'll be okay, girl. Whatever it is, it will be fine."

"Larry, I'm sure you will understand…"

"Understand what?"

"I'm accepting an offer to work for $PROH_2O$ as a factory salesperson. Billy will be calling you as well. I just need security and things are looking a bit rocky at Connection."

"I get it Emily. You're doing the right thing."

"I am?"

"Absolutely!"

"What are the chances of you taking Frank's old job and still being my boss? They hinted that you might be doing exactly that."

"I don't know, but I've committed to making a decision by tomorrow morning. I'll keep you in the loop."

Emily held back more tears as she sent Larry an emotionally charged plea. "You're the best boss I've ever had. I hope you understand it would be a lot easier to head down this road if you were coming with me."

"You're amazingly loyal. Thanks for all your support. Just remember that regardless of how this all ends up, we'll still be friends. I'll work on cutting your final check. Please send me any pending expenses."

"You're the best, Larry!"

Because Larry was immersed in life changing decisions of his own, he had not given nearly enough thought to Emily's emotions and feelings. He scolded himself for not helping Emily through her struggles. Finally, he rationalized that he had been negligent before that conversation but that everything worked out in the end. As he stared at his shaking hands, he was reminded of how fragile human beings are, how fragile Emily was, and how fragile he was. Nonetheless, that portion of rebuilding a relationship, a life, and a career was over. He pushed himself to move forward, turning his attention to his other employee. "Hi Billy, looks like we're heading down separate trails, my friend."

Billy excitedly replied, "What makes you think I'm going back to work for $PROH_2O$?"

"Didn't they offer you a job?"

"Yes, they did. But I don't want to take it. I want to work for you."

The counter area suddenly quieted down which relaxed Larry a bit. "I'm very flattered that you would want to take the plunge with me, but right now I don't have the resources to pay me, let alone you."

"No problem, I'll work for free."

"I can't ask you to do that, Billy. Take the smart trail and go to work for PROH$_2$O. They're a sure thing; Connection is a big maybe."

"I can get by without a paycheck."

"I know that, but I wouldn't feel good about that kind of arrangement."

"You don't understand!"

"Understand what?"

"Forty years ago I missed a huge opportunity. I don't want to blow another one now."

"I don't get it!"

"When I was in high school, I was part of a garage jazz band. I was one of the trumpet players. The other horn player spent a weekend with his parents in Tijuana, where they attended a festival of toreadors. When he returned from his trip, we got together. I skeptically listened as he excitedly told me that he had an idea for a new sound that celebrated the pageantry of a bull fight. He played a few bars before I interrupted him. I shook my head in frustration and uttered words that have haunted me my entire life, 'Your crazy idea will never work. I'm quitting this group.'"

"I need some help here, Billy. For some reason, I'm just not connecting the dots."

"Larry, my friend's name is Herb Alpert."

"The Tijuana Brass?"

"You got it."

"Holy shit!!

An exasperated Billy continued, "Holy shit is right!"

"So you're telling me that you don't want to miss another opportunity?"

"You got it!"

A steady stream of customers entered the counter area, increasing the noise level dramatically. Larry grabbed the portable phone base with one hand and the big black receiver with the other and entered the adjacent restroom to get away from the escalating background noise, "Billy, I'm not Herb Alpert and Connection Sales is not the Tijuana Brass. It'll take lots of pressure off me to go it alone. I love that you'd jump into a boiling stew with me, but I need to scrounge around the territory to find meat to replace the stones in my pot."

Billy scratched his head and said, "What?"

"Evidently you don't know the story about stone soup."

"Larry, I still don't get it."

"Please take that job with PROH$_2$O. Just know there's a good chance our paths on the trail will cross again."

"Okay boss, if that's the way you want it."

Larry, still locked in the restroom, hung up the phone, took a deep breath, and plowed forward. Next piece of business: Dial the number to PROH$_2$O.

An assertive voice answered the phone, "Hon Do Lee."

"Hello, Mr. Lee, this is Larry Schafer. I see you have paged me."

"Mr. Larry, I am most grateful that you have returned my call. We have now secured the services of Emily and perhaps Billy. We are awaiting your response. Please understand that we are very eager to have you provide necessary leadership for our salesmen. Do you have any questions about our most generous offer?"

"No, Mr. Lee. Everything is quite clear. I'll call you tomorrow with my decision."

Larry hung up the phone and paused, ever so happy to have that call behind him. Now it was Susan's turn. "Hi, just got your page. What's up?"

"Larry, I can't believe you did it again."

A knock on the restroom door triggered a move back to the counter area, phone base and receiver in tow. "Did what?"

"You know exactly what I'm talking about. You're going into the water heater business without discussing it with me. Don't you think I should have a say in a decision that could turn our whole world upside down?"

Larry wasn't expecting this kind of phone call as he stood at the chaotic wholesale counter. Plumbers were ordering from their material lists, hastily scribbled on ripped pieces of cardboard or castoff two by fours. "Sorry for all the noise; I'm at RP Supply."

"That's great! I imagine you're talking to everybody about water heaters."

Larry again turned his back away from the counter activity and replied with a quiet, muffled voice, "Susan, I've made no decisions. How could I make a decision without talking to you?"

"That's exactly what I was wondering."

"Let me guess, Mayor Sam told you that I was going into the water heater business?"

"Exactly!"

"Mayor Sam heard it from Sal who only heard half of my conversation with Red. Yes, Red and I discussed water heaters, and selling water heaters may in fact be the best choice available, but all I'm doing is talking to people in the industry I trust so that I can make the best decision possible."

"So, we will discuss this tonight?"

"I promise you, we'll talk and figure it out together."

"Okay, Larry!"

Larry was emotionally spent and it was only 9AM.

The next call was to Clarence Silverman, a prominent and influential repair plumbing contractor in Los Angeles who Larry knew well. Frank said that the L.A. repair market was a key ingredient. Perhaps Clarence would provide the much needed insight into the replacement water heater business. Larry's relationship with Clarence started when Larry engineered a private label program for Silverman Plumbing that featured the company name and phone number engraved on the flange of a kitchen sink basket strainer. The advertising was designed to make Silverman Plumbing memorable every time a homeowner rinsed out their kitchen sink.

Lunch was on with Clarence amidst a barrage of dots to connect. Larry was on a fact finding mission, trying to apply logic to the water heater business, something that Frank warned him not to do. He was equal parts scared, excited, and frustrated. A commitment from Red to support Larry's possible venture into water heaters had not yielded a willing distribution partner. He still needed to do some soul searching with a sharp pencil and yellow pad, and most importantly, talk to Susan!

Happy to be away from the RP Supply counter, Larry shuffled to the parking lot. As he climbed into his cherished van, it occurred to him that regardless of which offer he took, and which plunge he would take, his old friend the Astro would be headed to the scrap yard and he would start the slow process of making friends with a shiny new replacement.

CHAPTER 9

"Socrates"

As Larry drove west on the San Bernardino Freeway towards the heart of Los Angeles, he thought about Marsha's comment. Were the screws in his head really coming loose? He feared she might be right. Were he and the Astro on the same path? Then he thought about Mr. Petersen, a straightforward man who communicated his thoughts bluntly. Why did Mr. P coyly tell him that he might be getting a phone call? Questions were plentiful; answers were scarce.

A huge red sign featuring the Silverman Plumbing logo interrupted Larry's daydream. After using an intercom to gain entry to the headquarters of the largest plumbing repair enterprise in the city, Larry maneuvered into a tight parking spot.

Silverman Plumbing employed scores of professional, squeaky clean plumbers who serviced Los Angeles in boldly painted orange trucks. Clarence Silverman, the owner and industry legend, greeted Larry in the parking lot. "Based on your misfortunes with $PROH_2O$, you won't be replacing this Astro soon, will you?"

"It all depends on how my new venture works out. It looks like I'm going into the water heater business."

As was their ritual, the men conversed while leisurely walking to Mervin's Place, a popular Jewish deli, which was two short blocks from Silverman Plumbing.

As the men turned the corner, Clarence remarked, "Leave it to you. I love your resilience! I hope you're the new rep for National!"

"No, an established brand would be far too easy. Independence Water Heaters is the line I'm considering."

"Never heard of them!"

Larry's brain scrambled through limited data in search of a sales pitch about water heaters, a business different from any he had ever been involved in. "Independence is a smart newcomer that's competitive, made in the USA and does NOT sell to your retail competition."

As they walked across Culver Street, Clarence replied with a brutal honesty, "You sound like a football coach reciting tired clichés at a press conference."

The business friends arrived at Mervin's Place. A man pushing a shopping cart stood in front of the restaurant. His eyes begged for pity. Clad in countless layers of baked grunge and desperate for spare change, he held out a tin cup. Clarence stopped to work out a win-win of sorts. "What's your name?"

"Stanley."

Clarence handed him a dollar and offered a deal, "Okay Stanley, stay clear of this restaurant until nine o'clock and I'll see to it you get a plate of hot food at closing time."

Stanley made no comment, but nodded and moved on.

The men squeezed into the crammed deli. Four long lines that led to windows manned by smiling, happy workers with blue hats and bright eyes. As usual, the line moved efficiently.

The cashier greeted Clarence, "Hi boss."

"I'll take the Reuben sandwich with potato salad and a medium coke."

Larry was next, "The lox platter and a medium root beer, please."

"My treat Larry, but I'll let you handle the tip."

The men sat next to the window, placing their order number on the table and continuing the conversation.

"I would drive across town to eat at this diner even if you and Mervin didn't own it."

"Customers tell us that this hole in the wall fills a void in the tummy while energizing the spirit."

"You are a mensch, Clarence! A true mensch! What you just did for Stanley was huge!"

"It also helped Mervin's Place. Men like Stanley make most people uncomfortable. That's bad for business, bad for our goal of providing a getaway from the harshness of reality. Bottom line: Stanley and I compromised."

"Since he's loitering illegally, you could have called the police and have them deal with Stanley."

"Then everyone loses."

"I also think you just became his only friend."

"That might be true. Life can be cruel! If a man doesn't have reserves to get him through tough times, life can even be torturous!"

"I wonder how life became so hard for him."

"That's hard to say. Did the system work against him, or did he reject the opportunities presented to him? Who's to say?"

Larry couldn't resist being Larry. "You sound more like a Republican than a Democrat."

"There are pragmatic Americans in both parties."

"Agreed!"

"You and I generally find a way to create a win-win. I think it's because I move to the middle from the left and you move to the middle from the right. The aisle that separates us can be bridged easily with a handshake."

"Well said! You and I can usually find a way to meet the truck halfway."

"That's an interesting expression."

"I'm pretty sure Red Starr, my friend who owns Town and Country Plumbing, coined it."

"I've heard wonderful things about Red. He sounds like the kind of man I'd like to meet."

"I'll arrange it one day."

"Great."

"So, can I change the topic to water heaters?"

Clarence smiled. "You know I love talking business. Who stocks this new line of heaters?"

"Nobody, yet."

"Are you warehousing them here in L.A.?"

"No, everything ships from Michigan."

"You're a pretty good salesman, but even you might have a tough time selling a product that customers can't easily get their hands on."

"You're right! I do need distributors, but wouldn't it be to your advantage to buy a product not sold at retail?"

"Perhaps, but who's to say your new factory wouldn't, in time, change their mind and sell the product to big box stores? Everybody else does!"

"I've been assured that they have no plans to go retail, but even if they did, you'd be no worse off than you are now."

Lunch arrived, temporarily suspending the conversation. Clarence took a huge bite out of his sandwich. "Without question, best Reuben in town!"

Larry loaded cream cheese onto his bagel then added capers, tomato, and onion before capping the open face sandwich with layers of lox. "Since you own this restaurant, why do we always wait in line?"

"This is every man's restaurant. When Mervin and I are here, we are 'every man' just like everybody else. Look at the happy faces. Even old grouches smile at Mervin's Place. These customers just paid a premium for lunch, but because the food and service are consistently good, nobody ever complains. Deli sandwiches are a perfect retail product. As for water heaters, only professionals should be installing them. A bad Reuben sandwich might cause indigestion. If a homeowner, without 'know-how', installs a water heater he purchased at Bob's Big Box, he could blow up his house and perhaps do bodily damage."

"You're right about that. I've seen stuff like that on the news."

"Plus, hardware stores compromise my profits. As you can see from the prices we charge here at the deli, I love big margins!"

"Great! Sounds like you'll buy Independence Water Heaters as soon as I get you a distributor."

Clarence ignored Larry's attempt at a trial close. "How about commercial water heaters? There's a huge, profitable market for them in the city."

"We have the commercial models you install every day."

Larry's cookie cutter reply screamed for a comment from the business mogul, "You're serving up a Reuben sandwich without the corned beef and minus the potato salad!"

Since Larry didn't know the meat and potatoes of the water heater business, his only play was to deliver big picture philosophy. It didn't work, not with Clarence Silverman!

Larry tactfully shifted the conversation. "How would you compare the faucet business with the water heater business?"

"No comparison. When people are struggling to pay their bills, they'll live with a dripping faucet. It's a pretty sure bet that a leaking water heater will be replaced."

"You've got that right!"

"The water heater business is as steady as the deli sandwich business."

Larry nodded, "I'm getting my education on the fly."

The shrewd businessman took Larry under his wing. "Let's start with the basics. All water heater manufacturers produce commercial products. That's where they make their money. The key is to have a design that easily replaces an existing heater. In Los Angeles and in the San Fernando Valley, a product that has the exact dimensions and hook-ups as the National is a must!"

"How about the other brands you replace?"

"They don't exist; not in this market! Ninety-nine percent of the commercials in town are Nationals."

Before exiting the restaurant, Clarence commented to one of his employees, "A drifter named Stanley will be here at closing. Please fix him a nice hot plate."

"Yes sir!"

Upon return to Silverman Plumbing, Clarence invited Larry into his office and commented, "How about a cup of coffee?"

"Absolutely! You are quite the gentleman! I'll do some homework to make sure our heater will easily replace a National. In addition to a distributor, what else do you think we need?"

"A centrally located L.A. warehouse full of your heaters! It just so happens there's a building available that would be perfect!"

"I don't suppose you own that property, do you?"

"You know me too well. My building has easy freeway access and two loading docks. It just came onto the market."

"Sounds good."

Clarence added a squeeze of spicy mustard into the conversation, "This building would give you a local presence. It would put a new-comer on the map. This building would be great for Independence!"

"You're pretty passionate about this proposition."

"Using Red's expression, it's a great way to meet the truck halfway."

"Clarence, you never cease to amaze me! How do you do it? You and Mervin own the best deli in Los Angeles plus you own and operate a plumbing repair empire respected by everyone. And then, evidently in your spare time, you gobble up property as if you're playing the game of monopoly! Wow!"

"Every aspect of business intrigues me. Do you know why I'm partial to rental property?"

"I'm sure it's a good investment."

Clarence set Larry straight! "It's far more than that."

"Okay."

"Let me explain. You're a hard worker, but answer this question: are you making any money while you're sleeping?"

"Well, no."

After pouring Larry a cup of coffee, Clarence returned to his position behind his giant desk, leaned forward and made his point, "The key to financial security is to be involved in something that makes you money while you're sleeping."

"And real estate is one of those things, isn't it?"

"Of course! It is paramount to build wealth and deposit it into a variety of buckets."

"I get it, but I'm sure you agree that money doesn't necessarily buy happiness."

"In a world of few givens, that's a certainty. You don't seem to have any trouble making friends. You've taught me the importance of having friends in the plumbing business. I'm giving you dollar and cent advice."

"Thank you. I hope I can fill a bucket one day."

"You'll fill many. You hide your resourcefulness by playing the role of a student thirsty for knowledge."

"I don't know. It seems like I'm forever struggling to separate smart trails from dumb ones."

"There you go again; pretending to be less than the shrewd businessman I know you are."

Larry offered nothing but a smile.

Clarence continued, "I don't pass along my philosophies to fools. If a man is a fool, sadly he must learn from his own mistakes."

Larry was incredulous. "Few people would believe that your truckloads of wisdom share space with toilets and sewer pipe."

"All fools are not plumbers and all plumbers are not fools."

"Maybe Socrates was a plumber?"

Clarence laughed. "Unlikely!"

"What a combination: a plumbing empire mensch who has a hand in real estate, philosophy, and Reuben sandwiches."

"I'm a simple plumber; no more, no less."

"Okay then, from a plumber's point of view, how smart is it for me to go into the water heater business?"

"I think you know the answer to that question and I'm certain you know where to go and who to see. Relying on the guidance of your most trusted friends will be critical."

"That's why I'm talking to you!"

"Water heaters are a big ticket item. Since reps work on a commission, it has to be gratifying to know even a small percentage of a big number can be substantial. Every time you shower, you'll be reminded that there's no water like hot water."

"Sounds like you believe water heaters are a *Jelly Bean in Life*."

Clarence took a sip of coffee and paused. The timing was right to take full advantage of his leverage as both clever broker and potential buyer. "Please tell the Independence people I'll be very flexible on lease terms. How about my deal on these heaters: will the factory be flexible with me?"

"Once I get a distributor, I'll put together something attractive for you."

"Oh no! It needs to be far better than attractive. I'm a creature of habit and a big believer in proven winners"

"Like Reuben sandwiches and real estate."

"And National water heaters! Please remind the factory that Guinea pigs must be rewarded for their risk!"

Larry scrambled for pricing insight. "Do you have any idea what you're paying for a 40 gallon model today?"

"I'm sure you know what the price should be. Take that price and cut some fat off the corned beef."

"How about commercial water heaters?"

"Add extra sauerkraut to my sandwich!"

"You've always preached the importance of being profitable and complained about your price cutting competitors!"

"I always analyze a market before investing. Buying low and selling high is always the goal!"

"How about that win-win we discussed?"

"You're selling an unknown brand, Larry. Put yourself in my position!"

Larry clutched his cup of coffee and took a slow sip, "So you're not ready to reach across the aisle and shake hands?"

"You're smart enough to know that you have lots of work to do before I can commit to anything. You, better than anyone, should understand that clever solutions win the day. The faucet program you engineered for us has paid huge dividends — for both of us."

Larry smiled. "The faucets on your trucks were selected based on the size of their cartons."

"That's right, in our infinite wisdom we only inventoried the faucets that would fit in our truck bins."

"Unfortunately those faucets weren't the ones your customers wanted to buy."

Clarence nodded his head. "Exactly! But you had a rather clever solution that offered us the faucets our customers wanted in the carton sizes we needed."

Larry laughed. "When I submitted the proposal to change the

dimensions of our packaging, the factory was certain I had lost my mind."

"But you finally convinced them to do it and then I put your faucets on 125 trucks."

"We reached across the aisle and shook hands!"

Clarence smiled. "It was a true win-win!"

After the men shook hands, Larry slid behind the wheel, recapping the meeting with Clarence in his scrambled brain. He put his Astro into drive and continued his inner soul searching. In this solitary meeting he made random point after point to himself countered by rebuttals to himself. No words were spoken but there were gestures aplenty: eye rolling, head shaking, nodding and random hand signaling. All in all, Larry neither won nor lost the battle with Socrates. Nevertheless he headed east on the Pomona freeway with a mixture of exuberance and frustration, anticipating a return to his office by 2 o'clock. His meeting with Clarence reconfirmed that his friends were willing to give his water heater line a chance provided he ramped up his knowledge. Without understanding the business of water heaters, negotiating compromises would be difficult; suggesting clever solutions would be impossible.

Seventy minutes later, Larry was back in Lake Mathias. As he turned up Penny Lane, dots swirled wildly in his head. The pile of questions was growing while answers became increasingly elusive. What about the offer from Karl to go into the wholesale business and work in the office next to Brenda? Would it make sense to be a competitor of Russ Petersen, the man he respected just as much as Red, Frank, and Socrates? What about the Chinese $PROH_2O$ proposition? In his head, he had ruled out taking Frank's old job, but suddenly he even questioned the wisdom of that decision. At least he knew the faucet business. He knew very little about wholesale distribution, and it was becoming evident that he knew painfully less about the water heater business.

CHAPTER 10

"The Dangling Conversation"

Larry made his way up Annie Oakley Road, turned onto Penny Lane, and parked in front of his barnyard office. Since Charlie and Sergeant Pepper were taking afternoon naps, Larry's arrival was unceremonious. Carrying a briefcase filled with questions, he walked into his scrambled office and sat down at his makeshift desk. Stacks of boxes stared at him; begging for attention. First things first: calling the number to the ranch 100 yards away, atop the hill.

"Hi."

Susan smiled and replied, "Hi! What corner of the world are you in?"

"I'm here."

"Here...where?"

"Here! Here in my office. That's why I'm calling you. After attending a philosophy class taught by the plumbing Socrates, it's become increasingly evident that I've got lots of stuff to figure out. After I make a few phone calls, I'll be up for a glass of wine."

"Sounds great! So guess what?"

Larry was bewildered. "I have absolutely no idea."

Susan rolled her big eyes. "Of course you don't, but I'm going to tell you without making you guess."

"That's generous."

"I'm just in the mood to be a giver."

Larry was astounded. "Well, that sounds really...really good."

"It's taco night."

"Great!"

Susan continued, "But wine and tacos are much like 'couplets out of rhyme'."

"Now you're sounding like Paul Simon."

"Yes, Larry! I stole that line from 'Dangling Conversation'."

"Is this conversation dangling?"

"Stop being Larry! I'm suggesting margaritas and tacos."

"Perfect!"

"And Larry, just one more thing…"

Larry squirmed. He was happy about the margaritas and tacos, but now it sounded like there would be a condition attached.

Susan continued with a mixture of emotions, "I'm not sure which of your ideas was craziest: going into the rep business five years ago, or staying in it now. You cherish independence and I crave security. Those trails lead opposite directions in life. However, in spite of my wishes for stability, for some insane reason, I'll travel whatever trail you pick, side by side with you."

"Really?"

Susan coyly replied, "Well, maybe!"

Larry's emotions traveled on an imaginary elevator directly to the penthouse. "So you won't give me a bunch of crap about what I decide?"

"I didn't say that. I said maybe."

Larry acted like he was frustrated, but really he was having fun. "I need a translator."

"You're putting words in my mouth. Perhaps I should clarify."

"I love a clear picture!"

"I won't guarantee a free ride, but I'll join you on that trail. But…and this is a big 'but'…if you insist on being difficult, the deal is off."

Larry struggled to balance two conflicting emotions: shock and euphoria. Susan had just carved a direct route into the spot where he was most vulnerable: his heart. With choked-up words he uttered, "How in the world do you do it?"

"Do what?"

"When I get myself to the end of a trail, you come to my rescue. You gather the resources required and magically build the bridge I desperately need."

"You have such a way with words. Perhaps the answer to this quagmire is that instead of being a businessman, you pursue writing."

Words suddenly became as hard to connect as the elusive dots swirling in Larry's head. He struggled to piece together a meaningful thought. That failing, he replied with the simplest sentence he could compose, "I can't wait to have a margarita with you!"

Susan held back her tears. "I love you."

Enough was enough. Larry was an emotional wreck. He was at a breaking point! Then, finally his next move came to mind: a play he used whenever he felt most vulnerable. It was not a magic pill, nor was it profound. Clarence was Socrates. Larry? He was just Larry. Since he was a desperate man, he countered with the only tactic that made even a little bit of sense. He resorted to humor. "Even though I'm a Republican?"

As usual, Larry made Susan smile, even during an emotional firestorm. "Well maybe."

"See you in a bit."

Susan pondered an array of questions to herself. Would their different paths always end on the same trail? Would an independent romantic ever find the trail he was looking for? Why was Larry's body deteriorating, seemingly before her very eyes.

CHAPTER 11
"The Water Heater Party"

L arry hung up the phone in slow motion. Because it takes time for the heart to connect its dot to the brain, Larry paused. He sat like a statue in a park until inner peace overcame him; the inner peace Susan had provided. Her ability to guide him through tough parts of the trail was uncanny. He smiled, stretched, and refocused on a business at hand. While sorting through the coiled mountain of faxes covering his desk, the phone rang, "How was your day of water heater exploration?"

"Hi, Frank. You weren't kidding when you told me not to apply logic to the water heater business. Have you ever had a water heater discussion built around Reuben sandwiches with a philosopher?"

"You're flat killing me, Larry! Listen to me! I'm about to tell you something that may shake up the water heater industry and at the same time open doors for us."

"Are we having a jelly bean promotion?"

"Nice try. Stop being Larry and listen to me, you square headed German. There are four manufacturers in the water heater business, but one of the four, Copper Tank, has been struggling for quite some time and is rumored to be on hold with their steel suppliers. I would expect their distributors to start looking for a new water heater supplier."

Larry immediately thought about Mr. Petersen's mysterious comment about staying close to the phone. "That explains one of my big questions."

"What?"

"Sorry, I was just thinking out loud. One less competitor in a market is always a positive, provided it's not us!"

"You're right about that, but I wish you'd stop setting tables with jelly beans and Reuben sandwiches!"

"By the way, for us to get Clarence Silverman's commercial business, we need to throw a generous amount of sauerkraut into the pot."

"You really are killing me, Larry!"

Larry ignored Frank's comment. "Another question: Will our 100 gallon products easily replace our competitors' models?"

"Where that gets important is in the L.A. market. Our commercial models are a perfect replacement for the National."

"Same height and width; same vent size and water connectors?"

"Didn't I just say that?"

"I guess so. Does Independence pay distributors three dollars to unload water heaters?"

"Of course! Everyone does that."

"Well, I guess that makes sense even though the whole idea sounds absurd."

"You did it again, Larry"

"What?"

"You're applying logic to the water heater business."

"Distributors tell me they rarely change water heater lines, but if I have somebody on the hook, I need to have pricing and rebate information."

"I faxed it to you! You don't think I'd send you out to sell water heaters without the essentials, do you?"

Larry scrambled through the maze of faxes and located Frank's. "Okay, I've got it right here."

After a pause, Larry returned to his agenda. "Socrates tells me a local warehouse is critical."

"Who?"

"Clarence Silverman."

"I'm not even going to ask you why you called him Socrates."

"I've got a perfect building in mind for that L.A. warehouse!"

"What L.A. warehouse?"

"The one we need!"

"When you start selling 100,000 water heaters a year, I'll take a warehouse into consideration."

"But our customers can get any brand they want by sending a truck to a local warehouse that has water heaters stacked to the ceiling. How will I compete with that?"

"You'll figure it out, Larry. But you're asking way too many questions and getting miles and miles ahead of yourself."

"How can I be miles ahead when I feel hopelessly behind?"

Frank let Larry's train roll past a confused station. When Larry was being Larry, Frank had no choice but to push the ignore button. "So, Larry, do we have a deal?"

"Let me figure stuff out. Questions and answers are rolling around in my head like tumbleweed."

"I'm going to take that as a yes."

"Please take it as a definite maybe. I still need to talk to Susan before she changes her mind, get with Russ Petersen about an opportunity knocking, and attend another Reuben sandwich class taught by Socrates."

"As usual, I have absolutely no idea what you're talking about."

"I also need to connect dots with Red, Steve at Dick's Plumbing, and Big Ben."

"Larry! Its 2:30! How in the hell are you going to get all that done today?"

"That's a great question, Frank, but right now I'm looking for answers."

"It sounds like we're both searching for answers."

Larry hung up the phone, paused, and called Steve. "We talked about me coming up to see you, but I'm sorry, I just can't make it all the way up to Ventura today."

"Now you've done it! You've turned into a typical L.A. sales guy. You fall in love with mega numbers and forget about your friends up here in the sleepy beach town of Ventura."

"Steve, you know I love you. In fact, I love you so darn much that I'm going to trust you with my future."

"You even talk like an L.A. sales guy. Any chance you can translate that for me?"

Larry laughed. "It looks like I'm going into the water heater business. I know you've always distributed Hot Spot Burners, but can I twist your arm and get you to look at a new brand of water heaters called Independence?"

"It will cost you dearly."

"I will gladly pay it."

"You'll need to take a trip to Ventura and buy me lunch at Johnny's Beach Bungalow, and then maybe I'll think about it. Maybe!"

"I'll call you to set it up. Thanks a million for supporting me, and of course, Independence Water Heaters."

"I think we have a bad connection, Larry! What did you say about water heaters?"

"That's it, Steve, you heard me. Connection Sales is your connection to Independence Water Heaters!"

Both men laughed a laugh that only longtime friends can share.

"If you find time to squeeze me in, call me!"

"Expect a call, Steve. Thank you!"

Next on the list was to call a driving force in his life. If not for Big Ben, Larry would never have met men like Frank, Red, or Clarence.

"Hi Ben."

"For a guy that didn't want to be in the business of plumbing, it sounds like you're doing okay, Larry."

"Well, I was until my contract with $PROH_2O$ was terminated by the new owners. But it looks like I'm going into the water heater business."

"Do you still remember how to slap those puppies in?"

"Yeah, Ben, I think that was the easy part. It looks like the tough part is selling them."

"I think you'll do just fine. You've made enough friends to make a go of just about anything."

"Thanks. I'll be selling a new brand called Independence."

"Will they be available at Dick's?"

"I think so."

"Sounds like you need a little help. I'll talk to Steve. I'll make sure he brings them in so that I can buy them and save your ass! It appears that saving your ass is a cross I must bear in life."

"You're the best, Ben. Thank you."

"I just want to make sure you stay in the plumbing industry."

Larry philosophically replied, "There are days when I wonder if being in the plumbing industry is a blessing or a curse."

"Don't tell me you're cutting and threading pipe again."

"That's a good point. Even after a long, long day, I don't smell like cutting oil."

"There you go. That's a plus. I saw enough of you standing over that threading machine to know that you, like water, are not compatible with oil."

"Doing that job at Dick's brought a great appreciation for my father who toiled in a factory as a machinist his whole life."

"First hand experiences trump theory from textbooks."

"Now you're sounding like my friend Socrates."

"Who?"

"My friend Clarence. A plumbing philosopher like you."

"I'm not a philosopher; I'm your friend."

"You've been like a big brother to me. It's just that things are a bit challenging right now. Sometimes I feel like a piece of pipe when the jaws of the machine make their cut."

"I suspect you're winning more battles than you're losing. Don't lose sight of the bigger picture."

Larry paused before replying, "Thanks for filling my empty bag with jelly beans. Stay tuned. We'll talk soon."

Larry's mind was in Ventura when his phone rang again.

"Connection Sales!"

"Larry, this is Russ Petersen."

"Hello Mr. P."

"You were smart to stay close to the phone. I'm in the market for a new water heater supplier. Can you swing by in the morning?"

"That is, without a doubt, the best news I've heard in a long, long time. How about 7 o'clock?"

"That'll be great, Larry. Also, please verify that Independence supplies their residential product with a top T and P."

"I'll have an answer when I see you in the morning."

Larry immediately called Frank. "It's me again."

"Hi, you again."

"Very funny, Frank. Do our residential water heaters come with top T and P tapping?"

"We manufacture product for the rest of the country with side temperature and pressure relief valves, but for the west, we supply top T and P."

"Why is the T and P location different here?"

"It has to do with the plumbing code. In the west, the T and P piping must exit thru an outside wall and then drop down. Elsewhere, the discharge is directed straight down. There are times a side T and P would require plumbers to run pipe all the way around a water heater and then through the outside wall. A top T and P can be easily piped any direction. Other manufacturers have tried and failed to sell side T and P in the west."

"I thought I had my hands full learning the minute details in the water heater business that don't make sense. Sounds like there's a pile of stuff I need to learn that actually does make sense. By the way, I made my mind up. Connection Sales will be your new rep. I just need to tell Susan what I've decided and make it sound like it was her idea."

"Great plan!"

"I have a meeting with Russ Petersen in the morning. He just might be my first distributor. Can you join me?"

"Sorry, Larry, I'm flying to Denver and then to the factory for a meeting, but you can call me with any questions up until 9:30."

"But Frank, Russ will surely have lots of questions that require answers I won't have."

"Just call me if something comes up. Quit pestering me and go to work. Believe it or not, you're not the only new rep I have. There are seven agencies coming aboard at about the same time, and most of them have never sold water heaters."

"So I'm not the only rep trying to find logic in an illogical business?"

"You're killing me, Larry!"

After Frank's parting shot at him, Larry quickly called Silverman Plumbing. "Hi Clarence, this is Larry."

"I doubt you've had enough time to fill your briefcase with the clever angles needed to reach across the aisle and shake on a deal."

"You're right, but I think I'm headed down the right trail."

"Independence is not interested in my building, are they?"

"Not yet. It will be a topic of discussion when I start selling 100,000 units a year."

"The old chicken and egg game."

"You're probably right. By the way, since you're a philosopher: which one did come first?"

"Don't forget about the rooster! He's a big part of the question, and the answer."

"Makes sense! But I do have some good news. Independence commercial water heaters are the same height and width as Nationals. They also have the same vent size and identical top water connections."

"That's a start, but only a start. Once you establish distribution, we'll figure out the rest."

Larry added a positive spin, "I've already got an idea to add some extra sauerkraut to the Reuben."

"And make sure the price is as lean as Mervin's corned beef!"

"I understand."

Clarence continued his probing. "By the way, has Independence figured out a way to make a flue damper that actually works?"

"What's a flue damper?"

"Time for your next lesson. Flue dampers are designed to open when the heater is operating and close when it's not. Unfortunately, the dampers on Nationals have a mind of their own."

"When I was in college, I installed commercial heaters with my friend Big Ben. I don't remember them having flue dampers."

"Factories were forced to add them to meet new energy codes."

Larry shook his head in dismay. "So government mandated the changes that create these headaches!"

"You're starting to catch on."

"Sounds like a problem the Democrats brought to plumbing."

Clarence corrected Larry. "If George Bush would have read the letter I sent him, flue dampers would not be a topic of conversation."

"You sent a letter to the president of the United States?"

"Get me a sample of your flue damper, Larry."

"Yes sir!"

Confusion reigned. Larry's head spun as if he had just staggered off the Tea Cup ride at Disneyland. He hung up the phone and grabbed the faxed pricing and program information Frank had sent him. He briefly glanced at them. They appeared to be written in a foreign language. Was it Italian? They looked more like legal briefs than sales documents. He coiled the sheets in reverse and slipped them into his brief case.

After his spinning head slowly stopped its rotation, he got up and opened the Dutch door. Sergeant Pepper was already in position, quietly waiting his turn.

"Here you go, Sarge."

The stallion methodically emptied Larry's hand full of jelly beans.

"In spite of my battle to answer an endless stream of questions, I'm moving forward. I'm taking the plunge!"

The Sarge shook his head with a determination to send a message.

"I know, I still need to talk to Susan. Wish me luck."

Larry headed up the driveway with a spring in his legs that only served to make his heart beat faster. Charlie slowly picked himself up from yet another nap and greeted Larry as if to say he better have more answers to offer Susan than questions.

Right on cue, Susan walked out to the patio with margaritas in both hands. As she handed him his drink, she planted a kiss on Larry's surprised lips. As they sat down, Larry started the ball rolling. "I have a question for you. If I told you that Frank sweetened the pot by offering me a mobile telephone and a new car, what would you say?"

"What would I say? I'd say Frank must have been transformed into Mary Poppins. Are you serious?"

"Yes, I really couldn't believe it either."

"So now you're being auctioned off to the highest bidder?"

"Not really."

Susan smiled. "Sure sounds like it to me."

While Charlie snapped at a fly, the Schafers' lips tasted the salt on the rims of their Margarita glasses chased with the sweetness of the mix and the gentle bite of the tequila. Larry continued, "I have more good news. RP Supply is interested in my water heaters. Even Red doesn't know that."

Susan raised her eyebrows as she replied, "There's actually something I'll find out before Red?"

Charlie, like a town crier, started barking and made his way to Penny Lane to greet surprise guests. After tying their horses to hitching posts at the barn, Mary and Red reached the top of the driveway. Mary offered an explanation for their surprise visit, "Sorry to barge in on you guys, but we were out for a ride and just had to stop and say 'Hi'."

A very perky Susan rolled out the welcome mat. "Our home is your home!"

As they made their way to the patio, Susan continued, "So Red, what do you think about Larry going into the water heater business?"

Red, sensing he was about to step in a pile of horse dung, tread cautiously. "That's hard to believe. Ratchet doesn't even know if a heater is shaped like a cylinder or a rectangle."

"Really Red? That's all you'll fess up to?"

"Oh, I guess I heard a little bit this morning, but it seems like Sal knows more about it than Larry."

"Okay, I get it. We'll move on to happier trails. How about a Margarita?"

Mary didn't hesitate. "Sounds terrific, let me give you a hand."

While the women headed towards the kitchen, Red turned the conversation towards Larry. "So Ratchet, are you starting to figure out water heaters?"

"Not really, for every answer I get, five questions pop up."

"You're making this way too hard. Think about it! A tea kettle heats water much like the 40 gallon models you'll be selling."

Larry stopped and thought about Red's comment. It really was true. He shook his head and replied, "You plumbers sure are smart!"

"If we were smart, we wouldn't be the first ones on a job and the last one off of it."

"I had lunch today with a plumber I call Socrates."

"Socrates? What did he have to say?"

"That all plumbers are not fools and all fools are not plumbers!"

"What in the hell does that mean?"

"I think it means that some plumbers are smart and some are dumb."

"Well shit, I could have told you that. I've always tried to hire the smart ones and encouraged the dumb ones to go to work for my competitors."

"I think you're onto something there."

"Ratchet, I think you stand a better chance of learning about water heaters if you talk to plumbers instead of philosophers."

"I hear you! By the way, do you have any idea what you pay for a 40 gallon water heater?"

"Too much!"

"How much is too much?"

"$112 hard earned dollars for a juiced up tea kettle."

"I thought Ernie did the buying."

"Ratchet, you've re-programmed me to keep an eye on important shit!"

Susan and Mary returned with Margaritas. The four friends took a seat under a ranch umbrella as Susan offered a toast, "I told Larry that I'd support him on whatever decision he made; as long as it was the right one."

Larry studied Susan's face as she desperately tried to keep a straight face. After reading Larry's panicked face, Susan smiled and added perspective, "God knows the trails we've traveled on together haven't always been smooth. But with Larry's stubborn will and a bit of luck, things just might work out!"

Mary, who had quietly watched the conversation proceed down a bumpy trail, offered a toast, "May the sweetness of our friendship offset the Tequila's cactus-like bite and fuel the spirit in our hearts."

Susan quickly responded, "I think that toast is a preview of the column we'll all read in tomorrow's newspaper."

Red shook his head. "I told Ratchet it was sure interesting living with a journalist."

Susan replied, "Between Mary and Larry, I'm thinking you are never bored."

"Yes, my life is crazy but I guess I'm in need of even more craziness. I told Ratchet that if he actually does go into the water heater business, I'd be his first customer."

Larry smiled. "Thanks, Red. You know I appreciate your support."

"Don't thank me; thank Susan! If she wasn't providing adult supervision for you, there's no way in hell I'd head down that trail with you."

Charlie barked again. A bright white Dodge Caravan with new license plates was coming up Penny Lane. Moments later, it parked next to the vintage 1958 Corvette.

Susan was incredulous. "Larry, if you would have told me we're hosting a water heater party, I would have prepared more tacos."

Charlie greeted the latest guest, Frank Caparelli, as he got out of the car. Margarita glasses in hand, four curious onlookers quickly stood in front of the shiny new van.

Frank reached out to Larry. "Here are the keys to your new car. The mobile phone is already hooked up."

Larry was as happy as Charlie when he got a juicy bone. "Frank, I really don't know what to say."

"Try real hard to just smile and say nothing. That would be nice."

There was no way Larry could be silent. "I just called you an hour ago to tell you that I was accepting your offer."

"I know, but I'll be out of town for two weeks so I wanted to bring the car over before you broke down somewhere south of nowhere. This Caravan has been sitting in front of my house, just waiting for your final acceptance. I knew you would come on board eventually! Your phone call this afternoon was strictly a formality. By the way, for the next 18 months while you get your feet on the ground, Independence will also pay for your gas."

Red's exuberance could not be contained, "Wow Ratchet! Only you would land in a bucket of shit and come up smelling as sweet as Susan's Margaritas. How in the hell did you swing a deal that lands you a van with a phone, free gas, and customers waiting in line to buy a new line of heaters you know nothing about?"

CHAPTER 12

"Root Beer"

Larry quietly headed to the driveway. His Caravan awaited his arrival. He and his new van were like lovers on a rendezvous. He easily slipped behind the wheel, greeted immediately by that unmistakable new car smell. He familiarized himself with the gauges, seat adjusters and stereo. He had studied the manual of the car phone and felt confident on its operation. He called the number to his office for a test. It rang through loud and clear. After his answer machine picked up, he hung up.

He thought about the sleepless night he had just fought his way through: rolling over side to side, thinking about his sales call on Russ Petersen; pondering the challenge of overcoming obstacles on trails yet to be named. When that dream drifted away, he dreamed of the Caravan and the new mobile phone. It was a busy night to be sure. Sleep? He wasn't sure he got any, but that was okay. He would operate on adrenalin, caffeine, and the raging fire lodged in his belly.

Larry slowly guided his new transportation down Penny Lane and parked in front of his barnyard office. His mind bounced from topic to topic like a checker player making a four jump move. Now the water heater business again took the stage. It had become a challenging brain-teaser comparable to the Rubik's Cube. Larry recalled the childhood struggles of being an immigrant in a new country with a new language. As he entered his office and started the coffee brewing, he thought about the difficult trail ahead, but was quick to remember how his family had persevered through trails far more daunting. Connection Sales was short on staff and financial resources but long on bulldogged determination.

Larry acknowledged that even the Sarge was no stranger to challenges that were long on odds and short on hope. After taking a soothing first sip of brew from his comforting Ventura mug and offering Sergeant Pepper his jelly bean reward, Larry seamlessly moved into storytelling. "Only you would land solidly on all four hooves after being discarded like a pair of old socks with holes in them. I'm not sure who's happier about you living here with us at the ranch, you or Charlie. Of course, I don't have to tell you that Susan and I are partial to you as well. How does it feel to be living here with us on Penny Lane, light years away from a glue factory?"

Sergeant Pepper kicked the bottom section of the split Dutch door he was facing, with a very pronounced thud. A slamming sledge hammer would have been overwhelmed by the violent crash collision of the stallion's right hoof and an innocent bystander: the latched door.

"You've now lived with us five glorious years, right here at the ranch, in this barn which is becoming as tired as we are. There are many, many trails in life that are dead ends. The hope for anyone embedded with a love for persevering and embracing the spirit of God's greatest gift, the gift of life itself, is to stumble upon a trail that leads us to our reward. It's been tough going, the last four years, but remarkably we are enduring. Perhaps we're hanging onto a thread consisting of dots yet to be connected, but nonetheless, we are enduring. The ability to endure was instilled into my brother, Otto, and me early in our lives.

"In the first decade of rock and roll, long before the Beatles landed on American soil, my family embarked on a one way trip across the ocean to a land of freedom and hope: America, a nation whose Bill of Rights promised opportunity to anyone willing to work their ass off for a better life. We neither expected handouts, nor received them. We asked only for an opportunity. America delivered that opportunity. Our family embraced the American way of life and the American dream with grit and determination.

"Shortly after finding jobs in a factory, Papa and Mutti, enrolled in night classes to learn the language and earn American citizenship. That was amazing in itself because Papa's formal education in Germany ended at age ten. The citizenship test was in a foreign language called English. The questions involved details of the U.S. Constitution and the Declaration of Independence. Most first generation Americans would have flunked that test, but aided by unflappable determination, my parents passed it to become American citizens.

"My brother and I were immersed into school, sink or swim. Survival required that we learn the English language on the fly and fend for ourselves. Waking up, dressing, and walking to school for a punctual arrival, were up to us. On the way home, we scrounged around the neighborhood searching for soda bottles that we redeemed for two cents each. The money we earned paid for luxuries like baseball cards, movie tickets, and glazed donuts from the Helms Bakery truck.

"Being a stranger in a strange land wasn't easy, Sarge, and based on yesterday, figuring out the water heater business certainly won't be easy either. But nothing truly worthwhile comes easy. Our trail was full of challenges. In some cases our family backtracked after finding yet another dead end, but every step backwards was countered with two steps forward; most of the time, anyway.

"Our departure from Munich was in late November, 1956. We boarded the train that would take us to the airport on a typical cold and wet morning. I was five and my brother was nine. We were definitely dressed for the occasion: long underwear, a sweater, snow boots, an overcoat, and a cap that only an immigrant would wear.

"Papa had purchased our tickets with borrowed money and a burning passion to start a new life. As the Trans World Airline passenger plane lifted above the Munich skyline, we waived good-bye to our tiny apartment on 'Gulden Strasse' and our favorite family spot, Hirsch Garten, a sprawling park filled with old men playing chess and kids kicking soccer balls. I could almost hear festive polka bands playing Bavarian folk music as jolly patrons celebrated a lifestyle built around sausage, pretzels, and beer. Yes, Sarge, we said good-bye to our homeland.

"Fifteen hours later, we landed in Los Angeles. As we walked through the terminal, Papa let us know how much he craved the first taste of beer in his new home, the United States of America. After exchanging our German marks for U.S. dollars, we approached a vending machine. The coin went in and an American beer, called root beer, was dispensed. Papa wasted no time. He just had to celebrate our arrival to a new world with a beer begging to be sipped.

"But Sarge, that first swig resulted in our first dead end trail in America. Had we possessed the necessary funds to return to Munich, we would have undoubtedly taken the next flight home. I still remember the horrified expression on Papa's face as he spit out this, so called, American beer. His comments, translated from German, are engraved on the walls of my square head: 'If this is the beer they have in America, we are returning home'.

"After a barrage of exasperated homespun Bavarian profanity, we regrouped. That was the first lesson I can recall of accessing and regrouping. We continued on to baggage claim to collect the two suitcases that represented not only the sum of our possessions, but the necessary tools to survive in a new world. Papa was a sheet metal worker. One of the suitcases was filled with the tools required to work at his trade. He did not bring American language skills onto the airplane, but did pack a means to earn a living and provide for the family. The second suitcase was filled with everyday silverware, crocheted table cloths and a bushel full of hope.

"We were quite a spectacle. Not even Hollywood movie stars received this much attention. Imagine four immigrants dressed in variations of drab gray, prepared for freezing rain or a blizzard. As we walked out of the terminal we anticipated a need to button up our overcoats and bundle up. You should have seen the looks on our faces when we encountered our first experience with hot Santa Ana devil winds. Temperatures were burning hot. We were as out of place as 'Frosty the Snowman' in a Southern California brush fire."

The stallion shook his head and perked his ears.

"Okay, I know you have your own stories about overcoming adversity, but do you know what I call the shit that God throws at us?"

Sergeant Pepper again kicked the Dutch door with authority.

"I know you are probably thinking that the answer is horseshit, aren't you?"

The Sarge kicked the door yet again.

"Actually, the shit that God throws at us is nothing more than life itself."

CHAPTER 13

"Mr. P"

Larry and his brand new Dodge Caravan were parked out of harm's way, in the far corner of RP Supply's pipe yard. Larry had considered calling Frank from his Connection Sales office before leaving the ranch, but quickly scrapped that idea because Frank would not appreciate a call at 5:30 AM.

From his Caravan, Larry watched an abundance of activities: forklifts busy loading lifts of pipe onto bobtail trucks; plumbers picking up material, coffee, and donuts; tractor-trailers lining up to make scheduled deliveries. Larry rehearsed his approach for the critical meeting with Russ Petersen with marginal success. He looked at his watch. It was 6:30 and time to put his brand new phone to work. He needed to call Frank to pick his brain. He needed ammunition for his tool chest. It was still a bit early, but he proceeded anyway, rationalizing that the abuse forthcoming would be well worth the critical insight received. He crossed his fingers and dialed. "Good Morning!"

"Now what?"

"I just wanted to thank you for the Caravan and the phone."

"You're calling me at 6:30 to shower me with appreciation? Somehow, I'm not buying it!"

"Well, I do need some help!"

"Remind me to never hire you as a rep ever again, anywhere, anytime for any product!"

Larry calmly replied, "Yes sir. I just entered that note into my Franklin Planner."

Frank slowed the rhythm of his delivery and raised the pitch of his voice, "So, Mr. Schafer, how can I be of assistance. As you well know, I have been placed on this earth solely to serve you."

Larry ignored Frank's sarcasm, remaining unfazed and on point. "I reviewed the price sheet and program you sent me."

"Yes!"

Larry continued, "Red said he pays $112 for a 40 gallon water heater. I did the math. There's absolutely no way a distributor can sell our heater at that price, to a contractor like Town and Country, using the price sheet and rebate information you provided. The numbers don't add up."

Frank's response was matter of fact, "Sounds like we need to work up a new SRP sheet or perhaps work up a new quote for your territory."

Larry was puzzled. "What's an SRP?"

"Special Regional Pricing."

"The faucet business has one price for the whole country."

"That's correct."

"Water heaters have market price sheets?"

"Correct again. In markets where there is more new construction activity, we generally see lower pricing on key items."

"Like Southern California, I suppose."

"I know it's early, but it's taking lots of time for coins deposited into your vending machine to dispense understanding."

"Thanks for reminding me that I don't get it, but the water heater business might not be gettable."

"I'm not giving up on you yet, but I'm running out of coins."

Larry ignored Frank's sarcasm. "In other words, you're telling me that the price sheet you sent me is of no use whatsoever?"

"That might be true on 40 and 50 gallon gas-fired product, but we should be in good shape on the other items."

"I've only been at this for a couple of days, but it seems like the models that are the best sellers are the 40 and 50 gallon gas heaters."

"That's correct."

"So the price sheet is irrelevant on the models that matter most?"

"Well, you're probably right."

Larry was befuddled. "That makes absolutely no sense at all."

"There you go again. You really need to stop thinking so logically."

Larry was on a mission. "How about the distributor rebate program?"

"It's based on volume and market conditions."

Larry scratched his head in dismay. "So it's also negotiable."

The program I sent you is our standard, boiler plate program."

"Let me guess! There's a zero probability that the standard program will be attractive to RP Supply."

"That might be true."

"So you expect me to convince Russ Petersen to become a distributor for us without knowing anything about local pricing or territory rebates?"

"Bingo! 'Understanding' just penetrated your thick skull and was dispensed!"

"And you're the one that always tells me that I'm killing you?"

"This is a great learning experience for you. Now you know exactly how I feel when you're killing me."

"I don't know how to respond to this craziness."

"You'll figure it out."

"The only thing I'm certain of, is that I know nothing about Independence and even less about the water heater business."

"That's really not true Larry. Were you not listening when I told you that we are American owned, American made, and that we don't sell to retailers?"

"Yes, and I also understand we have a 5 year warranty, like everyone else, and that we, like our competitors, discount every water heater $3 for what's called an unloading allowance. I can't believe that water heater people haven't figured out that the customer will need to unload their shipment whether we pay them $3 or not."

"You're still applying logic to the water heater industry. Are you a no-hoper?"

"Well, you did just say I was as dumb as a soda machine."

"Big deal!"

"Russ Petersen eats up reps and spits them out!

Frank ignored Larry's ranting. "While you're developing your sales strategy, don't forget that you've also learned that the specifications of our commercial water heaters will serve you well for the replacement business in the L.A. market."

"That's right Frank! And I learned that we are the only water heater manufacturer that does NOT have local inventory and that everyone has problems with flue dampers, even though I know very little about them. By the way, I'm sending you a request for some samples of our damper."

"Focus on the positives, Larry! Since you're adept at finding jelly beans buried within deep crevices of confusion, staying positive should be easy for you. I assure you that you'll learn to love the water heater industry and, just maybe, thank me for dragging you into it. My guess is that the water heater business will, in time, be quite lucrative for you. As for flue dampers, don't worry about them right now. Just know they're a nuisance for everybody." Frank paused before continuing, "And Larry..."

"Yes."

"Ask Russ Petersen lots of smart questions. That's the best way to understand the market in your territory. Furthermore, always remember that no matter how much grief I give you, I've got your back and that Independence will do whatever is necessary to keep your customers competitive. Have you figured out how to use that new phone I just got you?"

"As a matter of fact I have. It's very cool. Learning to use that phone was a lot easier than figuring out the water heater business."

"So you applied logic to learn how to use the new phone?"

"No shit, Frank! That's exactly what I did."

"Perfect. Now just do the opposite. Learn to think illogically and you'll become a water heater expert in no time."

Larry scratched a head teetering between the logical and the illogical. At wit's end, he exploded, "So you're telling me that I need to use illogical logic in the water heater business?"

"God knows you're a square-headed German, but I think you just might be catching on. There's a silver lining in this discussion: look how much you've learned about the water heater business in two days."

"Okay. I get it. You're right."

"So Larry, since you know how to use that new phone, call me after your meeting with Russ Petersen."

Larry was trying to stay calm, but it wasn't working. "That's it? That's all the help I'm getting on pricing and rebates?"

"You have a way of thinking on your feet and rising to the occasion. That's why I hired you."

"But Frank…"

"Gotta go, Larry. Good luck!"

Larry paused in silence as he stuffed pricing information and random thoughts into his briefcase. Unconnected dots ricocheted within him. He looked at his watch. Oh my! It was time for his meeting with Mr. P. In a fraction of a moment, he changed gears and located a hidden bundle of resolve. He replaced unknowns with big picture perspective.

Larry shook his head north and south as larger dots began connecting. He really appreciated Frank negotiating a program to get him the new van, transportation that rode smoother and quieter than the Astro by a long shot. The seat was firm and as comfortable as his favorite chair at the ranch. Since he could easily slide into the driver's bucket seat, instead of climbing into it, the wear and tear on his back was reduced dramatically. And then the phone! Yes, the phone! The mobile phone was the best sales tool he had ever possessed. Efficiency! Larry worked hard all day, every day, to efficiently do his job. That was part of his German upbringing. Since he could spend less time in the office and more time in front of customers, his efficiency had jumped dramatically.

The snapping of the the clasps on the brief case punctuated Larry's mission. He sharpened his focus as he walked through the front door of RP Supply without a sign of the sleepless night he had just endured. He pushed the logic of the illogical aside and went to work. He poured a cup of supply house coffee into a tiny cup and secretly added sprinkles of determination and confidence. "Hi Marsha."

"My oh my! Who fixed the loose screws in your head?"

"I have absolutely no idea what you're talking about."

Marsha rolled her eyes as she buzzed Russ Petersen to get the blessing that would allow Larry into his chamber. She then turned to Larry. "Mr. P gave you the green light. Good Luck!"

Larry turned the corner into Russ Petersen's stately office. "Hello Mr. P!"

"So you've made the decision to plunge into the water heater business?"

"Yes. I would love to tell you I'm an expert, but the fact of the matter is that the knowledge I possess would fit into this tiny Styrofoam cup. The water heater industry evidently holds hundreds of gallons of illogical ironies that make no sense whatsoever."

"Well, Larry, it takes lots of guts to sit here with me trying to sell something you know very little about."

"I'm not sure if I'm here because I'm gutsy or stupid. I'll let you be the judge of that."

"I'm well aware of my reputation as being tough. However, I'm sure you know that I've always worked well with reps I respect."

"Yes sir!"

"When we met yesterday, I had a feeling I would be looking for a new line of water heaters. So here we are. You're looking for a customer and I'm looking for a new supplier. Tell me what you've learned since yesterday."

Larry took a small reassuring sip from his tiny cup. "Thank you very much for the opportunity. I have a commitment from Red to buy Independence Water Heaters. That's the thing I'm most certain of. Beyond that I need to be candid; we have no local warehouse, which means we ship from our factory in Michigan and our lead times average three weeks. However, we have lots of positives. The thing that convinced me that Independence is a winner is they are American owned and do not distribute through retailers. We are wholesale only and have a complete line that includes a commercial heater that easily replaces existing units in your market."

"That's all interesting, Larry, but I hope you don't think I'll give you a million dollars of business based on that. You really don't have local inventory?"

"That's correct."

"Well, that must mean you have some aggressive prices that will get my attention. Let me take a look at your price sheet."

Larry handed Russ the price sheet Frank had faxed him. Mr. P stared at the sheet with disgust; raising his eyes and focusing on Larry over the top of his reading glasses, "Surely you don't expect to do business with these prices!"

"No I don't. You asked me for my price sheet. You didn't ask me what pricing we would actually take to the market."

"Larry, because you're new to the business, I'm trying to cut you some slack, but you're making no sense whatsoever."

"I understand Mr. P, but do you think it would be logical for a rookie in the water heater industry to give you competitive prices for this area without doing some research?"

Russ Petersen was starting to lose patience. "So, Mr. Schafer, when are you going to do your research?"

"Well, I've done some of it. Red is currently paying $112 for a 40 gallon gas water heater. Understanding that you need to make a reasonable profit selling Red, what invoice pricing are you looking for?"

"That depends on your rebate. I don't suppose the factory gave you a copy of your program?"

Larry fortified his confidence with another sip. "Actually, Mr. P, I have it right here."

Russ glanced at the rebate program and shook his head in frustration, "Damn it Larry, first you give me a ridiculous price sheet and now you give me a rebate program that's 5% short. What in the hell is wrong with these people?"

"What if I got you that extra 5%? Would that put us where we need to be?"

"You need to be where I was with Copper Tank."

Larry calmly took another sip before asking for help, "Any chance you could share those prices with me?"

Russ again looked at Larry over the top of his glasses, "Is your unloading allowance also negotiable?"

"No Mr. P, we have a $3 unloading allowance."

"Are you absolutely certain that's not negotiable?"

"Yes sir."

"As I said, you're 5% short on your program. Additionally, you need to include a tiered incentive program: an extra 1% for reaching a million dollars in sales and an extra 2% if I miraculously buy two million dollars of your water heaters."

Larry frantically took notes as Russ continued. "Those additional incentives need to be calculated going back to dollar one."

Larry was familiar with that kind of structure because PROH$_2$O used similar wording. Russ confidently fed Larry another caveat, "You'll also need to add a 1% conversion allowance that will fund the sweeteners necessary to convert my customers to your unknown brand."

Larry responded, "I'm writing all of this down! Would we have a deal if I was able to package a program with those ingredients?"

Russ Petersen looked into Larry's eyes like a 'holdem' player trying to read the opponent's hand. "Not quite! You'll need to add a 2% promotional allowance!"

In this high stakes poker game, Russ Petersen held all the cards while Larry had no idea if Russ's proposal would be accepted or rejected by the factory. Nonetheless, Larry played his weak hand with an unfazed, determined confidence. "I'm pretty sure I can help you convert your plumbers to Independence in short order, so it might be logical to provide the 1% conversion allowance for the first year only."

"So now you're applying logic?"

"Yes sir!"

"Have you forgotten that nothing you've presented makes any sense at all?"

"No I haven't!"

"So you agree with me?"

"Yes sir."

"But you still want to pull that 1% from me?"

Larry took the final sip of coffee remaining in the tiny cup. "I'm merely trying to mediate a proposal that will be satisfactory to both you and the factory. I need to convince Frank that this deal is a give and take of sorts, and that you and I are meeting the truck halfway!"

"Okay Larry. But if you don't convert my contractors, we're going to have a conversation, a serious conversation. Do I make myself clear?"

"Yes sir."

After a silent moment, Larry continued, "As for pricing, is there any way you can help me out?"

"Is this part of your research?"

"Well, it would be really nice to know what prices we need to invoice you on 40 and 50 gallon models."

Once more, Russ looked at Larry over the top of his reading glasses: "$120 and $160!"

"Wow, that's a lot lower than the price sheet."

Russ shook his head in dismay. "That's exactly what I've been trying to tell you."

"So those are the prices you've been paying from Copper Tank?"

After a torturous moment of silence, Russ took a deep breath and confidently replied, "Yes!"

"Wow! No wonder they're going out of business."

Russ Petersen's next move was equivalent to a poker player going all in. "Reliable and Hot Spot Burner are also at those numbers, and they are very much in business; however, if you aren't willing to play ball, let's call it a day and I'll take my business to one of them."

"I didn't say no. I just need to call Frank to get this approved. I'm hoping there really is logic in the illogical. Please allow me to make a quick phone call."

"I really don't want you having that kind of a discussion in the presence of my people or my customers."

"Not to worry. Thanks to Independence, I now have a mobile phone. I'll make that phone call from my van."

"Larry, it's beginning to sound like these Independence people are quite generous. Throwing a mobile phone into my program will increase your chances of striking a deal with me!"

Larry grinned. "Please give me a few minutes, and I'll be right back."

"Make it quick, Larry, I have a ten o'clock tee time!"

"Larry hustled to his van and went to work with the urgency of a desperate 911 caller. "Frank, I may be on to something, but before I give away the farm and all the eggs, I need to run something by you!"

"You've got five minutes. As we speak, I'm parking my car at the airport."

"I have a proposal that might get us all of RP Supply's business."

"I'm listening."

"Russ needs an additional 5% on his rebate, an additional 1% incentive for reaching sales of a million dollars, 2% for hitting two million; back to dollar one. Plus 1% for converting his contractors to Independence during the first year only, and a 2% promotional allowance."

"Damn it, Larry, that wasn't a negotiation, it was an armed robbery! How about pricing?"

"He needs a quote for $120 on 40s and $160 on 50s!"

"You really are killing me, Larry! Hang on! I just put my car in park. I need to do some quick math. Do you think we can get the business if we agree to this rape and pillage?"

"He also requested a mobile telephone like mine."

"What?"

"Never mind the phone. Yes, I think we have a real good shot at securing the business. Don't forget that Mr. Petersen always pays his bills on time and that RP Supply is the target of every manufacturer in the business."

"If we write the business as you proposed, the company will be selling at a loss and I'll probably get fired!"

"I take that as a 'no'!"

"Don't put words in my mouth. I didn't say no."

There was a long, long silence while Frank punched numbers into his calculator. "Okay, we'll do it! If RP Supply agrees to give us 100% of their business, we'll write the program as proposed."

Larry backed down. "I don't want you to lose your job and I don't want the company to lose money."

"Don't stop selling until I tell you to stop! If you weren't such a no-hoper, you would have closed the deal already, but then again, you don't know a damn thing about the water heater business, so I'll be easy on you. However, it would be really nice if you finally got us a customer."

"I'm making my first official sales call, on my first official day, selling something I know nothing about in an industry that defies all common sense."

"Don't give me any of that first day bullshit. This is your second day!"

"You're not easy on a rep that's as dumb as a soda machine."

"Larry, don't give me any excuses! Just bring home the business and quit thinking logically!"

"Gotta go, Frank! Mr. P is headed to the golf course. I want to present this before he leaves."

Larry hustled from the parking lot, past Marsha, and down the hallway to Russ Petersen's office. "Sorry Mr. P, I couldn't get you the phone, but I got a yes on everything else. Fortunately, Frank was scrambling to catch a plane and didn't have much time to think about it."

Russ again lowered his chin and looked directly into Larry's eyes, over the top of his glasses, "Are you going to honor water heaters under warranty from Copper Tank?"

Larry had done his homework. The program Frank had sent him clearly stated that Independence would assume warranties provided a distributor made a 100% conversion. "Yes sir, provided you stay true to your one brand philosophy."

"Larry, I will remind you that I have been a Copper Tank distributor for over ten years. I always commit all my business to one water heater brand and I make it a habit of staying loyal to that manufacturer. I called Red this morning, before our meeting, to confirm his commitment to your water heater. I've always wanted to sell Red water heaters, but he's been loyal to the Hot Spot Burner, a brand distributed by my competitors. After I told him I was becoming an Independence distributor, he gave me a nice purchase order! I need to get myself to the golf course, but while you were on the phone, I made a quick list of product that I need right away. Write this up and put a rush on it. And don't give me any of that three week nonsense. I need this order by next Friday. Swing back by when I have a little more time, and we'll book some additional loads."

Larry was overwhelmed, but maintained his composure. He looked at the list Mr. P had given him. "Wow! Thank you very much! I'll get this going immediately. Just a quick observation. It looks like you're ordering 145 water heaters. It takes 150 units to get the $3 unloading allowance."

"Figure it out Larry. Call me to set-up our next meeting. Leave the purchase order on my desk, and don't forget to price it out. Also provide a written copy of the program we agreed on and be sure to get me my $3 unloading allowance on this order. Don't forget! I need these heaters by next Friday."

Russ shook Larry's hand and exited through a private door that led to the private garage he called his bat cave. Larry was in shock, standing motionless in disbelief. As he quietly celebrated, his mind swirled. How was all of this possible? Larry sat down in the lunchroom and wrote up the purchase order per Russ's instructions. To satisfy the factory's minimum quantity of 150 water heaters, he increased, by five, the quantity of forty gallon heaters on the order. Russ told him to figure it out so Larry went out on a limb and figured it out. If it was a problem, he would beg for forgiveness. He stopped by Marsha's desk to acquire a copy of RP's financial information that 'Independence' would need. The final step was faxing the order to the factory with the credit info and leaving a copy on Russ's desk.

Larry returned to the Caravan. Even though it was only 9:30, he was emotionally spent! The meeting with Mr. P was a graduate class in negotiation. Mr. P, provided he got the deal he wanted, had already made a decision to become an Independence distributor before Larry even sat down with him. The financial problems of Copper Tank opened doors. Nonetheless, Red was the key. Without Red, Larry would not have a purchase order in his hand. Without Red, Reliable or Hot Spot Burner would have been Russ's first choice. After all, they were entrenched in the market. Nonetheless, Larry and Independence prevailed. Closing a deal of this magnitude in an industry he knew little about, in whirlwind fashion, was comparable to a vending machine that dispensed miracles.

CHAPTER 14

"Hall Pass"

After processing his first order, on his very first official day as the rep for Independence Water Heater Company, Larry's spirits soared high into the stratosphere. Connection Sales, on the edge of extinction, had suddenly become viable. As he pointed his attention towards Los Angeles to explore possibilities with Classic Plumbing Supply, Larry began a series of calls to button up loose ends. Job one was to call Hon Do Lee, the new vice president of sales for PROH$_2$O. "Hello, Mr. Lee. Thank you for your offer, but I've decided to stay in the rep business."

Hon Do Lee was incredulous. "So you are not accepting our most generous offer?"

"No I'm not."

"I am sorry to hear that, Mr. Larry."

"If you'd like to keep me on your team, you can appoint me your independent rep for Southern California."

"Mr. Larry, we are committed to a strategy of factory sales people. The contract between Connection Sales and PROH$_2$O will remain terminated."

As Larry hung up, he felt a huge sense of relief. He now turned his attention to Westerly Supply. "Hello Karl, I appreciate your tempting offer, but I'm staying in the rep business."

"Since you lost your faucet line, what in the hell are you going to sell?"

"I still have some small lines that will cover my expenses, but I'll primarily be in the water heater business."

"Don't tell me that you're the son of a bitch that stole Red's heater business from me and moved it to RP Supply?"

"Well, I'm now the rep for Independence, and Red has decided to buy my water heaters from any distributor that handles my product. Unfortunately, Westerly is not an Independence distributor. However if you would like to stock my product, I can make that happen."

"Did you hear that sound, Larry?"

"No, I'm on a mobile phone and the reception isn't too good."

"I visualized you being my pencil and then I broke it in half!" Thanks for making this a crappy day."

Karl slammed down the phone, which triggered a reaction on the other end of the wireless signal from Larry, who instinctively pulled the phone from his ear and mumbled, "I'm getting really tired of being Karl's pencil."

As Larry headed east on the Pomona Freeway, his ever so popular phone rang. It was Susan. "I'm so glad you have a car phone. CHC just called me back. You have an appointment with Dr. General this afternoon at four."

"Who the heck is CHC?"

"Larry, why is it that you can remember minute details about every customer and the names of their children, but you can't recall who your doctor is? CHC is our health care provider, Community Health Care."

"CHC is where you took me after my rattlesnake bite five years ago."

"Yes!"

"And they're the people who insist on giving me hall passes."

Susan shook her head and replied with a sigh, "They're not hall passes. They are merely referrals that in time will yield answers."

Larry hated going to the doctor. Being around people with ailing bodies was depressing. He knew the answer to his flippant question, "Answers to what?"

"To find out why you and Charlie walk up the driveway huffing and puffing."

Even though Larry knew that Susan made his appointment because she loved him, he responded as Larry being Larry, "Should I bring Charlie with me?"

"Very funny!"

"Thanks for caring about me."

"Aren't you the sweet talker? You must be having a good morning."

"The score is two to one. I've made two enemies and one friend."

Susan took a deep breath. "That doesn't sound promising."

"A man hasn't lived a life worth living, if he hasn't made enemies worth having."

"Don't tell me you just pulled those profound words out of the glove box of your new car?"

Larry continued, "No, actually Will Rogers is credited with that quote. I'm pretty sure he was a Republican."

"If you intend to stay in business, I think perhaps you should work a little harder to even the score. As for your political commentary, just imagine me rolling my eyes."

"I've seen those beautiful eyes roll before, so it's easy to visualize. Anyway, I'm on my way to L.A. with a goal of evening the score."

"Okay, sweet talker, can't you tie the score in Riverside? I don't want you to miss your appointment."

"I'll be there! By the way, I have my first water heater distributor on my first official day in the water heater business and I'm learning the art of illogical logic."

"I always thought that illogical thinking was standard operating procedure for you."

Larry ignored Susan's comment and replied, "Russ Petersen committed his water heater business to me. I have a purchase order in my briefcase!"

"Oh, Larry. That's wonderful! That must be the friend you made."

"As a matter of fact, it is. The commission on RP Supply's business alone will get me closer to break even."

"So now you will lose less money?"

"Well, I guess you could say that."

"Sounds like you need a few more friends."

"It's really hard to get a second customer before getting the first one."

"I know that, Larry! Find a few more friends and this thing just might work out after all."

Larry hung up and looked side to side in a puzzled state of confusion. While he was on the phone, the Caravan was, seemingly, on auto pilot. He didn't know what highway he was on or what city he was in. For the moment, he was lost. While being immersed in his conversation with Susan, he had entered a twilight zone that defied all sense of time and space. Mobile phones were an unmatched convenience, but at the same time, scary as hell.

A freeway sign listing upcoming off-ramps put Larry's mind back on track. If Marsha, at RP Supply, would have seen him in that brief moment of confusion, she would, most certainly, have repeated her previous observation that Larry had loose screws in his head. One interchange and two exits later, he pulled into the parking lot of Classic Plumbing Supply.

An old friend of Larry's, Teddy Mack, was the buyer. Ultimately Larry would need to meet with the owner, Hans Schmidt, but perhaps Teddy would help him devise a plan of attack. Classic's largest facility doubled as the corporate office. Larry entered through a frantic will-call counter and poured himself a cup of supply house coffee. He would again use the secret weapon of having a cup of coffee at hand while asking smart questions the tactic Larry had used in his ground breaking meeting with Mr. P.)

By entering the gigantic general office through the will-call area, Larry bypassed the receptionist, whose job it was to screen visitors, like Larry, who had no appointment. The 'back-door' strategy gave him direct access to a maze of cubicles and offices. He knew that the people in that sales bullpen and the associates employed at Classic's seven branches would ultimately dictate his success or failure. He would start his water heater mission with the only person in the company he knew, Teddy Mack.

"Hi, Teddy."

Teddy looked up with a startled expression. "Well, if it isn't Larry Schafer. You must have sneaked in from the counter. You know all the tricks, don't you, Larry?"

"Not really, but I've had some pretty good teachers. It's sure great to see you."

"Quit the BS Larry. There are only two reasons you would magically appear in front of my desk. Either you're going to ask for a favor on some new line you just took on, or you want to use my phone. Let me help you out with the second part of that equation. No, you can't use my phone!"

Years earlier, when Teddy worked at Westerly, Larry was instructed by Teddy's assistant, to use the phone in Teddy's office to check on an order that Westerly desperately needed. When Teddy got back from lunch, he walked into his office only to find Larry sitting at his desk. After he pulled the receiver from Larry's ear he screamed words Larry would never forget, "If you ever sit at my desk or use my phone again, I will strangle you with the cord and throw your fat ass into the dumpster!"

Larry calmly sipped slowly from his cup. "Great news, I don't need your phone. I'm now the proud owner of a mobile phone."

"That's a relief! I really didn't want to stuff your butt into a dumpster anyway! So that means you're here to talk to me about a new line."

The stage was set to shake up the conversation. "My objective is to sell my new line of water heaters to Classic Plumbing Supply."

"You are one ballsy son of a bitch! You think you can just walk in here and sell us heaters? The only thing you've done that's dumber than that goes back to you making yourself at home in my private office."

"I didn't think it would be easy. That's why I'm here asking for your help. With your help, Independence will become the brand that will dominate the water heater market one day."

Teddy fired back, "Well, one thing hasn't changed: you're still full of shit!"

"Consistency is a virtue!"

"What brand did you say this was?"

"Independence."

"So you're a pioneer!"

"Correct!"

"You're exactly the kind of guy that ends up with arrows stuck in his fat ass! Leave it to you. Wholesalers rarely change water heater brands; not even to another established line. And you? You stumble in here expecting to sell a mysterious brand that nobody has ever heard of. Forget about it. It will never happen! Not in the water heater business! Not at Classic Plumbing Supply!"

Larry was undeterred. "It sounds like, with your help, we can do business."

"Yeah, right!"

"So if you were me, what would you do to get this line established?"

Teddy drifted back into the sixties and started reminiscing, "Well, in the old days, at Westerly, we used to sell water heaters truckload after truckload. I had every big contractor in Orange County buying them like crazy. The margins were tight, but I didn't mind because when I sold them heaters, I ended up getting all of their business. That's the way to do it. You've got to sell the big plumbers."

"What big plumbers does Classic Supply sell water heaters to?"

"We don't sell any of them. I'm just telling you how I used to do it. Man, it was fun. I would take those big plumbers out for three martini lunches, get their heads spinning, and then write all the damn business I wanted."

"It sounds like that strategy won't help me here, but I can tell you that Silverman Plumbing might be interested."

"Might be interested? What the hell does that mean?"

"It means that Socrates and I are working on a deal to reach across the aisle and shake hands."

"Socrates?"

"Yes, that's my nick name for Clarence."

"You operate in a cloud of confusion that's never been seen in this business!"

"I love being a leader!"

"Okay, Larry! Enough already! See that kid across the hall from me?"

Larry turned his head and got a peek at a young energetic man meeting with two colleagues while at the same time typing on his computer and talking on the phone.

"That's Roland Quick. He's one smart son of a bitch, but he's book smart. Hans Schmidt and I are teaching him the street smart side of things. When he gets that part, there will be nobody in the business that can touch him. Ultimately, you'll need to convince him, but you should start with Hans; he's the boss. He befriends smart reps but has no patience for reps that don't have their shit together."

Larry interjected, "He sounds like Russ Petersen."

"That's the first smart thing you've said. I know you're not that bright, so I think you hit something on the nose purely by accident. As you might remember, I used to work for Russ. I'm positive that Hans Schmidt and Russ Petersen were chiseled from the same chunk of granite! They are like the teachers in high school that nobody screwed with. It's never necessary for men like that to ever remind anybody who's in charge."

"My kind of guy!"

Teddy continued, "Hans Schmidt will pick your brain to see if you know your stuff. He will turn over every rock and investigate every sliver of information, process it and come at you from a point of view that will totally surprise the shit out of you. If you know your stuff and if he thinks Classic can make money on what you're selling, he just might, in time, have an interest in negotiating a program on your product. When he does that, he'll gift wrap his requests in such a way that you'll be certain that the deal, which is way beyond anybody else's deal, is actually justifiable. Your pocket will get picked by the best negotiator I've ever seen. And here's the irony. You'll actually feel damn good about it. But Larry, you'll really need to be patient. Reliable is our brand and I expect it to be our brand for a long, long time. A distributor has to have a damn good reason to switch water heater lines."

Larry was amazed, "Wow!"

Teddy was on a mission. He was the teacher. "This is definitely not Westerly. At Westerly we sold a shit load of water heaters to a short list of giant contractors. That was the meat and potatoes. The crumbs we left behind were insignificant to us. I keep trying to tell Hans and Roland how I used to do it, but they just don't listen to me. They're satisfied with the replacement business."

"I'm guessing there are lots of water heaters replaced every day in Los Angeles and that you guys are supplying lots of them."

"Okay, smart ass! You're right!"

Larry sensed it was time to get out of Teddy's School of Business. "Any chance you can buzz Mr. Schmidt? I'd like to meet him."

Teddy turned and immediately satisfied Larry's request. "Hans, I have an old friend here who wants to meet you. He's in the water heater business."

"Send him in!"

Teddy shook his head and grinned. "You heard the man. Good Luck!"

Larry flashed back to his school days when his favorite game was to get a hall pass: the vehicle that would provide freedom from a torturous classroom. After refilling his coffee cup at the counter, he walked down the hall and stood at the open door of Hans Schmidt's office before daring to go in. The office had the feel of a home library: friendly and relaxed. It created an ideal setting for having a meaningful conversation. And perhaps, negotiating the perfect deal.

Hans Schmidt acknowledged Larry and waived him in as he wrapped up a computer project. He then stood and shook Larry's hand. He looked at Larry's business card and laughed, "Connection Sales. You're the faucet king."

"Well, not really. You probably heard that PROH$_2$O terminated their reps and went with factory people. So now I'm in the water heater business. This is my first day."

"So Emily is no longer with you?"

"That's correct. She's back with PROH$_2$O as a direct sales person."

"She calls on Teddy. He always makes time to see a cute sales gal."

"That sounds about right."

Hans Schmidt laughed and looked at his watch. "So you've been at it about five hours?

"Yes sir?"

"Tell me what you've learned about water heaters."

"Really not too much, it's kind of been a crash course. But one thing has become pretty clear…"

Larry sipped a drink of coffee during a stage setting pause.

Hans Schmidt was eager to hear the answer, "And what's that, Larry?"

"Not to apply logic to the water heater industry."

Mr. Schmidt had no alternative but to wryly smile. "That's a good start. What else?"

"I sell Independence Water Heaters, which are American made and not sold at retail. Which, I guess, is a plus. Clarence Silverman is pushing me to get him a distributor and Town and Country Plumbing is already switching jobs to Independence."

"You've created all of this turmoil in five hours?"

"Actually, I was also at it yesterday, but today is my first official day. I've also learned that we have a commercial water heater that easily replaces existing units here in your backyard."

"Well, Larry, although Teddy thinks I'm foolish for not rewinding to the sixties, we make it a habit of staying away from big new work plumbers like Town and Country. But Clarence Silverman is in our wheelhouse. Since it's your first day, I don't suppose you have any distributors yet."

"I have one. RP Supply in Riverside."

Hans rocked forward in his chair and locked eyes with his guest. "My-oh-my, Larry! You don't mess around, do you?

"I believe in planning my work and working my plan!"

"So you're telling me that Russ Petersen jumped on board this morning?"

"Yes, sir!"

"Then you must have some pretty tasty prices."

Larry reached into his briefcase and handed Hans the price sheet.

Hans reached in his desk drawer and pulled out a Reliable Water Heater price sheet and compared it with the Independence pricing, "Well it looks like someone did their homework. These prices are pretty close to published market pricing. So you must know Red and Clarence?"

"Yes, sir."

"What does Red pay for a 40 gallon gas water heater?"

Larry took another sip of coffee, paused, and then replied confidently, "That would be confidential information but I will tell you that we'll always be competitive in the market."

"Your price sheet is competitive, but I'm pretty sure that you can't sell

Town and Country Plumbing using this price sheet."

"You're correct. That's our price sheet, but we don't necessarily sell our water heaters at those prices."

"You're pretty clever, Larry. I need to wrap my arms around all of this information that you've acquired in about a day. Are you having any problems with your flue dampers?"

"I've heard that flue dampers can be a nuisance. I'm really not sure if ours will be better, but I do know that if there's a problem with one, I'll go to the job site myself and take care of it."

Mr. Schmidt had spent his lifetime talking to reps. But Larry? He had never met anyone quite like Larry. "Where do you ship from?"

"Michigan."

"Do you have a local warehouse?"

"No sir!"

"Great. That's the best news I've heard."

"Really?"

"Yes. That means a stocking distributor wouldn't be competing with a guy who brokers your product. I hate it when manufacturers allow a non-stocker to send a truck across town to will-call."

Larry paused and replied, "I get it. Because the competitor would have no investment in inventory, they could, theoretically, undercut your prices."

Larry and Hans stared at each other during an awkward snippet of silence before Hans replied, "Exactly!"

Hans Schmidt stood up and reached to shake Larry's hand. "You've provided food for thought, Larry Schafer. Thank you for stopping by. On your way out, introduce yourself to Roland Quick."

After thanking Hans for his time, Larry headed down the hallway again, still clutching his cup of coffee and imaginary hall pass. The moment he stuck his head into Roland's office door, Larry realized that Hans Schmidt had given Roland a heads up. "Very nice to meet you, Larry. Call me for an appointment and we'll spend a little more time."

Larry got the picture. Hans Schmidt had put Larry smack in the middle of a good guy, bad guy 'play'. Larry gracefully accepted the message. "Have a great day, Roland, I'll be sure to call you."

Larry circled back to Teddy Mack's office, but no one was home. He then weaved his way through the office, past the will call counter and into the pipe yard. He knew Teddy was a chain smoker. If he wasn't in his office, he was likely outside the building satisfying his habit. Larry turned his head in the direction of the cigarette smoke and immediately saw Teddy standing between lifts of plastic pipe, clouds of smoke trailing behind him as he rested one foot on a pallet.

"Hi, Teddy!"

"How in the hell did you find me?"

"Just a lucky guess."

"How'd you do?"

"Okay, I think. Anyway, I didn't get thrown out. I have one more favor, please. There are about twenty people that work in this giant office. Any chance you can help me with their names?"

Eddie inhaled another menthol laced hit of nicotine. "Now you're pushing it!"

"Am I being tossed into the dumpster again?"

"You're damn lucky that I like you!"

Larry drew a rough sketch of Classic Plumbing Supply's office. As he rolled his eyes, Teddy helped him fill the names of the employees in the boxes, and their job description. "Are you done now!"

"Almost. How about your branch managers. Give me a feel for them."

Teddy pretended he didn't hear yet another request from Larry. He finished his cigarette, flicked it to the ground, and stomped on it. "My break's over, Larry. See ya."

"Teddy!"

"Alright already you pain in the ass."

"Which branch sells the most water heaters?"

"Probably Van Nuys."

"Which of your branch managers is most likely to buck your system?"

"The problem child in San Diego! Are you finally done with me?"

Larry was appreciative. "You're one hell of a guy. Thanks for the info on your people and teaching me about the water heater business. I also appreciate the hall pass."

"Hall pass?"

"Never mind, Teddy, I've got to get going. If you stick me in that dumpster, I'll be late to my doctor appointment."

Larry looked at his watch. He had planned three more calls, but because of traffic he needed to head back to Riverside. Even then, making the doctor appointment would be iffy. Since Susan had made the appointment for him, missing it was not an option. Even though it was wonderful to have Susan care about him, Larry was less concerned about himself and more concerned about getting a fledgling water heater business off the ground. As he walked to his Caravan, he quietly celebrated a pretty good day; the tally of friends was winning the game against his enemies by a narrow margin.

Larry got a break. Traffic was not too bad. After wiggling his way through a maze of freeways and arriving at CHC, he navigated through a series of hallways just in time to meet with Dr. General. That meeting was a bit longer than his chat with Roland, but certainly shorter than his meeting with Hans. Like everyone else that Larry had talked to about his weakening body, Dr. General was clueless. Larry was frustrated. It was unclear which of his challenges was more perplexing: water heaters or his very own body.

On his way back to the ranch, Larry went back to work. The next course of business was to make an appointment with John Brown of Quantum supply. "Hello John, this is Larry Schafer with Connection Sales. I would like to talk to you about Independence Water Heaters. Are you available tomorrow morning?"

"So this is the famous Larry Schafer from the faucet business?"

"Well, I was in the faucet business, but now I sell water heaters."

"How about seven o'clock. I always have time to talk to a faucet celebrity. Make sure you bring all your secret $PROH_2O$ rebate programs that I never got."

"John, you do understand that I'm now a water heater rep, not a faucet guy."

"That's what I like best. Now you can divulge the secret prices and programs I've been missing and not get into trouble for it."

"I'll see you at seven, John."

As Larry drove his shiny new Dodge Caravan slowly up Penny Lane, he drove past Sergeant Pepper, who was grazing in the pasture without a care in the world. Larry noted that the Sarge did not require a hall pass to navigate his life. It was always great to drive to the top of the driveway versus walking up the steep stretch and being reminded his legs seemed to get heavier every day of his life. All in all, it was great to be home at the ranch. Charlie slowly struggled to his feet as his tail started its windshield wiper motion. Today, was a pretty darn good day, but even on Larry's worst day, Charlie was a dose of sweetened medicine that made him smile. "Hi Charlie, how you doing old boy?"

Charlie raised his greying head and accepted a pat. Larry proceeded to the back door and entered the sanctuary that was the ranch.

"Honey, I'm home!"

Susan, dressed in Levis and a loose fitting Tee shirt, emerged from the back of the house with an enthusiastic, magical smile. "Tell me all about it, Larry."

"Well, after I listened to Teddy Mack tell me how he used to sell water heaters in Orange County in the sixties, I learned a couple things about how they're sold today."

"Not that, Larry. The doctor! What did the doctor tell you?"

"After the nurse sucked up a gallon of blood, Dr. General told me to see a different doctor, because evidently he really doesn't know anything."

"So you were referred to a specialist?"

"I hope so. That would be better than wasting my time talking to a doctor that just provides hall passes."

"Larry, did you tell the doctor about your inability to easily climb the driveway or navigate stairs?"

"Yes, that's exactly how I got the hall pass. I used a similar tactic with Teddy Mack at Classic Plumbing Supply."

CHAPTER 15

"Pear Blossom Highway"

After Larry eased the Caravan down Penny Lane to his barnyard office, the morning routine sprang into action. While the coffee was brewing, he opened the Dutch door and fed the Sarge his jelly bean reward. Larry filled his cup. As he took that first glorious sip, he wrestled with overflowing emotions triggered by a night of turmoil. "Sarge, a few hours ago, I woke up from a nightmare with my body soaked in perspiration and shaking. Thankfully, reality set in just before my body crashed into the seats above the 50 yard line. In this dream, the coach had implored Igor Krakeldorf to punish any player that stood in his way until they lost all will. 'Igor the Carnivore' reacted by exploding into me with a Herculean force that sent me flying helplessly into orbit like a rag doll."

Larry's sounding board stood motionless, seemingly in disbelief. After a long pause, Larry summed up the fantasy event, "I have a confession. The goal was met! While in free fall mode, I did lose my will!"

Sergeant Pepper shook his head as if he was confused. Larry looked his four legged friend in the eye and confirmed that both he and the Sarge were lost in a frazzled, hypnotic trance. Nonetheless, Larry continued, "Since I couldn't bear another jarring hit by Igor, even in a dream, I forced myself out of bed, went to the kitchen for a glass of water, and stepped outside to get a breath of fresh ranch air. I went back to bed, hoping my brain had been scrubbed from the ranting of the maniacal coach and his pet carnivore."

"My head gently eased into my feather pillow while my eyelids softly closed. Was a peaceful night of sleep now in play? Oh no, the nightmare continued! I was desperately looking for a hiding spot from Igor when I stumbled upon a forbidden door. A golden key magically appeared in my hand! I unlocked the door. Pandemonium carried me into a deep Ventura fog. I ran frantically up and down countless dead end trails, flailing at unconnected floating dots with a butterfly net. I turned from side to side in hopes of ending the trauma. What a night! What had I done to deserve this punishment?

"I shook myself before a third adventure invaded me! I was in a class at Ventura College taught by Socrates, who was lecturing students on the fundamentals of the water heater business and passionately proclaiming that it is a competition won by the team with the best strategy. The philosopher then climbed on his desk and threw a trash can, containing banana peels, apple pits, and wads of paper, across the class room screaming, 'SUCCESS IN THE WATER HEATER BUSINESS IS ONLY GRANTED TO THOSE WHO EMBRACE A FUNDAMENTAL PREMISE: LOGICAL THINKING IS ILLOGICAL!'

"While the students sat in horrified shock, Socrates climbed off his desk and made his final comments in a slow eerie whisper that every terrified student heard, 'Beware of the squeeze play! Squeeze plays are designed to catch you off guard and steal all that you own'. The ringing of my alarm clock at 3:45 punctuated the conclusion of a punishing night."

The Sarge was hopelessly lost in Larry's dreams.

Larry stopped and took another sip, replenishing his empty tank and setting the stage for big picture narrative. "On the home front, Susan is persistent about getting my slow moving body evaluated. God only knows where that trail will lead. As for Connection Sales, income is dribbling in from sales of Pull-Rite tools and Hub-Master test plugs. Hopefully, we'll still be receiving checks from $PROH_2O$ the next two months. With a little luck, water heater commissions will roll in right after that. Thank goodness I put away a few dollars four years ago. That small cushion may very well be the difference between Connection Sales surviving or being erased from the map. It just seems like I'm being squeezed in all directions."

Sergeant Pepper whacked a confirming blow against the Dutch door. As Larry wrapped up another soul searching morning with his four legged friend, he headed to his desk to check incoming faxes. "I'll be headed down the Pear Blossom Highway today, Sarge. The next sales call, I'm sure, will re-confirm the craziness of the water heater business."

After Larry processed five small orders, he patted Sergeant Pepper on the head and glanced at his watch. It was 4:30 AM and it was time to move the ball forward. Armed with his cup of coffee and brief case, Larry made his way through the night and into the Caravan. He sat behind the wheel and took a deep breath while taking in the soothing aroma of his morning brew. Through the gates of Penny Lane and down the dirt road he went. He refocused on the job at hand: discussing water heaters with John Brown, the master of the squeeze.

John was one of Larry's favorite people in the industry. He always looked forward to the visits with the eccentric industry legend. John operated miles off the plumbing business grid, both literally and figuratively.

After reaching a straight stretch of Highway 138, Larry made the first phone call of the day. "Hi Frank, this is Larry."

"No shit, who else would be calling me at this time in the morning?"

"I figured since you were in Denver, the hour difference would put us on the same schedule."

"Larry, its 6:30 in Colorado! My Denver rep is picking me up at seven. I'm just now jumping into the shower. What do you want? And make it quick!"

"I'm on my way to Quantum Supply to see John Brown. I just thought you would want to know that things are looking up and that I've stopped applying logic to the water heater business. Yesterday I met with Classic Plumbing Supply and took the first step in converting them. Unfortunately, it's probably a five thousand step process, barring a miracle."

"There you go sandbagging again! Larry, don't call me this early in the morning unless you have something more meaningful to report."

"Well, actually I do."

"Let's hear it!"

"While you were on an airplane flying to Denver, RP Supply became our first customer! The opening order is in house. I've been working with the girls in Philadelphia to expedite credit approval and shipping."

"Way to go, Larry! Get us a few more customers and I'll consider taking you off of probation!"

"Yes sir!"

"Keep the ball moving forward and let me get this old body into the shower."

"See ya, Frank"

The Caravan sped through a rollercoaster-like dip which splashed coffee out of Larry's cup and onto his pants. He swallowed hard to push his stomach out of his throat. He was on the Pear Blossom Highway and well on his way to Lancaster.

Larry mumbled to himself, "My strategy to wear dark colored pants on trips down the Pear Blossom Highway just paid a huge dividend. Nobody will ever know I showered my pants with coffee."

As he glanced at his watch, he noted that he was actually ahead of Larry time with arrival to Quantum Supply projected to be 6:30 for his 7 AM meeting. Larry planned to evaluate his schedule for the balance of his day after the Quantum Supply meeting. If it was a short meeting, he would work his way to Route 126 and head to Ventura. If it was longer, he would head south on I-5 and south on the 405 to make a sales call on Classic Plumbing Supply, Van Nuys. According to Teddy Mack, that location sold far more water heaters than any of their other branches. Then, there was option three. Larry had no idea what option three would be, but he knew John Brown well enough to know that a meeting with him could lead down trails yet to be named. Actions and reactions! Accessing and regrouping! Those were common themes in the life of Larry Schafer.

As the Caravan bounced up and down a bumpy segment of the highway, Larry's head nearly hit the headliner of the van. As his body slammed back into the seat, the phone rang. "Larry, this is Clarence Silverman. Have you found a distributor for your water heaters yet?"

"Hi, Clarence. I do have my first distributor, but they're in Riverside."

"I don't think a distributor in Riverside will ship water heaters to Los Angeles."

"Don't be so sure. I'm working on it.

"Sounds like there's a chance we'll be able to reach across the aisle and shake hands on a deal. Don't forget I will need a tasty program and delicious prices!"

Larry hung up the phone only to get another call. "Ratchet! Damn it! You sell me on these new heaters, and now I can't get them. Check on the order for RP Supply and rush it! You're killing me, Larry!"

"Got it, Red, I'll get them moving."

"And Larry, you are going to supply me with free heaters for the model homes, right?"

"Of course! I'll work on it!"

A third call came in behind that one. "So you forgot about your long lost friend Big Ben up here in Ventura. I can't believe I have to beg you to come up and see me when all I'm trying to do is help you."

"Okay, Ben. You're starting to sound like Steve. By any chance did Steve ask you to call me?"

Ben was silent for an eternal moment, "Why in the world would you say that?"

"Ben, please tell Steve that I'm working on a trip to Ventura. In fact, I might make it up there today. I'm in Lancaster. I'll call you after my meeting."

Larry turned the corner, crossed over a jarring set of railroad tracks and turned left onto Quantum Road. He drove a block, made a "U" turn and parked in front of a plumbing supply house disguised as a military Quonset hut. Sheltered by unoccupied buildings across the street, homeless people huddled in blankets. Larry grabbed his briefcase and slammed the door of the Caravan. He briskly walked to the front door of the business with purpose and determination, transitioning from the lessons of his nightmare to the Pear Blossom Highway…and now to the heart of 'The Squeeze'!

CHAPTER 16

"The Squeeze"

Larry walked through the front door of Quantum Supply. No hall pass was needed on this sales call. While many of their competitors were just rolling out of bed and thinking about their bowl of cereal, Quantum Supply was aggressively pursuing every potential order from every contractor on their radar. Since the housing crash had reduced the size of the business pie, their strategy was to squeeze into their competitor's portion.

As Larry eased into the chaotic office, the leader of the pack, John Brown, was finishing a phone call with one of his branch managers. John would ultimately end up in his private office, but he sat at that first desk in the bullpen every morning until about 9 AM. He was the greeter, cheerleader, supreme strategist, and most importantly, 'master of the squeeze play'.

A frantic sales team was squeezing numbers with the hope of securing an order. Larry walked through the drab, worn sales pit and poured himself a cup of coffee. Conversely, the mood was not drab or worn out. It was invigorating! It felt like the opening bell of a New York Stock Exchange war room. "Barry, listen carefully! Just tell Mel's Plumbing that, if he orders a full truckload, we can match that price. Here's our angle Barry. Write this down! As a sweetener, we'll give him a free relief valve for every water heater he buys."

John tilted his head sideways, hung up, turned around, and glanced at his watch. "And here's the faucet celebrity! You're early Larry. I like a man who is eager to do business." John Brown took a sip of his 'Caffeine Sally' coffee, "You know what Larry? I love these lattes. I'm sure the coffee people have added a secret ingredient that got me hooked on them."

"Really?"

"The coffee beans do come from South America. Sounds reasonable now, doesn't it?"

"So you are well versed on faucets, water heaters, and coffee?"

"Everybody has an angle. It's my job to uncover closely guarded secrets. I study everything that affects my life. Larry, these lattes, with the addictive infusion, sure beat the heck out of the coffee I used to pick up at 'Terrible Tina's Gas and Snack', but I really hated paying the latte price. The very thought of going from 49 cents a cup to $2.89 squeezed so much air out of me that I thought I would faint."

"The $2.49 did that?"

"Over-paying for anything makes me light headed."

"John, I think your stash of walking around money can cover the $2.49."

"This is no joking matter! I did the math! Multiply $2.49 times two cups a day times 300 days in a year!"

The numbers bouncing around Larry's head triggered a default mode, "Help me, John! How much is that?"

"In one year's time, Sally's coffee would cost me $1,494 dollars more than Terrible Tina's."

"Wow!"

"It's the law of big numbers!"

"What?"

"If you multiply a big number times even a fairly insignificant number, the result will be still be a pretty big number!"

"One thousand four hundred and ninety four dollars! Wow! That certainly is significant!"

"Yes, Larry! Yes!"

"So you squeezed them for a deal?"

"Have you ever wondered who sets up the patio umbrellas, tables and chairs at coffee houses in the morning?"

"Employees I suppose."

"Not anymore, Larry. Not at the local Caffeine Sally's. I do. It takes me about seven minutes to do the whole set-up just around the corner from here. What do you think I get in exchange?"

"Let me guess, John! You get a latte."

"A venti, Larry. They give me the venti. They offered me a grande, but I squeezed them a little bit and got the venti latte. See Larry, all these years I've been buying $PROH_2O$ faucets and I never got a venti latte. Not even a grande. I figure I've been getting the tall size filled halfway. I'm sure the big national guys are getting a venti latte filled to the top, a pastry, and a CD on every one of their orders. I think factories angle to squeeze me, so that they can afford to pay the big rebates to the big guys. How do you think I feel about an angle like that? Talk about a squeeze play. I'm tired! Look at my eyes! I'm dead tired!"

"So why do you stay in this business?"

"I like the action, Larry. I'm addicted to the action just like I'm addicted to the lattes."

John Brown was complaining about being squeezed while he angled to squeeze Larry. He continued, "I'm sure you've heard of Ray Brown, right?"

"The legendary jazz musician?"

"Right again Larry. You're starting to catch on. By the way, I took lessons from Ray Brown. He was my bass teacher, but that's a story from a different era." John stopped to let his mind return from a trip to his jazz playing youth. "Anyway, Larry, I want the Ray Brown special from $PROH_2O$."

"My head is spinning. What's the Ray Brown special? "

"The Venti latte, cannoli, and Ray Brown CD."

"I thought only coffee houses in Italy offered cannoli."

"They're not displayed in the window, but I'm pretty sure that coffee houses have a supply of cannoli behind the counter for the customers they deem worthy. Manufacturers do the same thing, providing perks for a chosen few. Because I'm way out here off the side road of a side road in a small town in the desolate high desert, I never get those secret deals. Am I right, Larry?"

"It's sure great to get an education John, but as I told you, I'm no longer in the faucet business; I'm in the water heater business."

"So the faucet legend is going to give me the Ray Brown special on water heaters?"

"Perhaps!"

"Larry, you need to talk to Leo Rodini from 'Water Heaters For Less'. He buys more heaters than anybody. Have you met him?"

"No I haven't."

As Larry answered, John was already dialing his speaker-phone. "Listen Leo, you've squeezed me so hard on heaters that I'm actually losing money on every one I sell you. I'm sending a guy named Larry to talk to you about water heaters."

"What brand are they, John?"

"It really doesn't matter, Leo. A water heater is a water heater."

"Are you and Larry making these new heaters in your garage?"

"Hang on, Leo."

"Larry, what's the name of these new heaters?"

"Independence."

"Did you hear that Leo?"

"No!"

"Independence, Leo. Independence Water Heaters. With this line you'll have a leg up on your competitors because they won't be able to find them anywhere else. Independence is a secret brand."

"How will the prices be, John?"

"When you see these prices, you will thank me for sending Larry out to see you. Hang on, Leo."

"Larry, can you see Leo right after our meeting."

"Yes."

"Leo, unlock your front door. Larry will be there to buy you breakfast and make you money."

John hung up the phone. "Let's talk about my prices and the Ray Brown special on your water heaters."

"Don't you want to hear a little bit about Independence before we talk numbers?"

"What could possibly make your water heater so special?"

Since Larry was dealing with a staunch and proud Italian, he called the appropriate play, "Well for one thing, they are headquartered in

Philadelphia, and the management team is Italian."

"So you're the token German?"

"Yes sir! And you're the only Italian I know that doesn't have a last name that ends in a vowel."

John ignored Larry's comment. "You're not selling them to national distributors right now, are you?"

"No, and we aren't selling them to the big retailers."

"So what I told Leo was the absolute truth. His competitors won't be able to get them."

"I guess that's true."

"Larry, I've done some calculations. Based on today's cost of steel, I figure a 40 gallon water heater costs about $64 to make. I'm going to be generous and let your unknown factory make 25% on me. That will make my price $80. I can sell them to Leo for $95 and everybody will be happy."

"Everybody except me, John. I won't be happy because if I give you that price, the Independence Italians will find a hole in the desert to bury me in."

"Now you're giving Italians a bad name. Get me a killer deal, Larry, and don't forget that there's no bottom to any market."

Larry was in the squeeze play of his life, gasping for air. "I'm not going to tell the factory that the market has no bottom. I don't think they really wanted to hire a German in the first place."

John didn't miss a beat. "Just remember I need the Ray Brown special. Leo is waiting for you. Here's his address. And, Larry, I'm right aren't I? I don't get the deal that the big guys get on faucets, do I?"

"John, if you bought the amount that they do, you would get their program."

"That's exactly what I thought. Nobody gives a hoot about the independent distributor trying to rub two nickels together so he can just get by."

"John, I'll call you after my meeting with Leo. What brand of heaters are you buying right now?"

"I buy all of them. Water heaters are a commodity. Don't bore me with details, just come up with some sharp numbers."

"John, we don't make these heaters in China or Mexico."

"Well maybe you should. That's where the cheap labor is. It's a competitive business, Larry. I need to have the right prices. Let me see your price sheet!"

Larry handed John the price sheet that was sure to be ridiculed.

"This is a joke, right, Larry? I don't have time for jokes. Give me your real prices."

"That is my real price sheet, but we really don't sell heaters at those prices. We also have a rebate program."

"That's what I figured! You're getting me a quote. I need a quote that is net-net, Larry! I don't want to wait for a rebate. You can bill me at that sheet and then let me take a deduction off the invoice at remittance. That will be my real price. Get it? Just remember, I know how much a water heater costs to make and I know there is no bottom to any market. And Larry..."

"Yes sir."

"Leo will be talking to you about stickers."

"Stickers?"

"Yes! Water heater stickers that can be converted into profits."

"Stickers with a clever angle?"

"Yes, Larry, yes! Get out of here and go see Leo, and don't talk to anyone but me about the deal we are putting together. You promise me?"

"Yes sir, this is between you, me, and Leo. Leo is Italian, right?"

"Leonardo Rodini is Sicilian! Just a word of warning. I know Leo pretty well. He is going to squeeze you, so stay on your toes! Do you know the difference between an Italian and a Sicilian?"

"Well, not really."

"The Sicilian carries a sharper knife!"

CHAPTER 17

"Stickers"

Armed with limited information about a Sicilian named Leo Rodini, Larry cracked open his Thomas Guide map book to route himself from Quantum Supply in Lancaster to the Valencia address that John Brown had provided. He wrote down turn by turn directions for himself, and also placed an encircled number on the map page, referencing it to 'Water Heaters For Less'.

As he drove over the railroad tracks that led him away from a typical mind-twisting and exhausting meeting with John Brown, Larry loosely weaved together his plans for the day. As usual, there were many dots to connect, and little time to connect them.

Since Valencia was located near the junction of Interstate 5 and Highway 126, a trip to Ventura was likely in the works. It would be about an hour drive from 'Water Heaters For Less', through the farming towns of Fillmore and Santa Paula, and into the beach community of Ventura. Larry maneuvered his Caravan through the maze of numbered and lettered streets that ran just as perpendicular as the high desert town of Lancaster itself.

Nearly every dot on every map is noteworthy for something, and the high desert is no different. For most travelers the high desert is the vast and boring chunk of desolate real estate separating Southern California from Las Vegas. Larry thought about the many times he had trudged through Barstow on scorching summer days and stopped for a burger, root beer, and gas. Unlike the typical traveler hungering for a casino, Larry's trips had a business purpose. Gamblers stash their pockets with a lifetime of savings as they dream about rolling the dice at a crap table praying for a hard eight, raising the bet in a 'Hold'em' game with a pair of aces, or doubling down at the blackjack table. But not Larry. His mind was typically occupied with thoughts of closing a big deal on a big job that would generate a big order.

As Larry headed down Sierra Highway, a formation of military aircraft reminded him of how important it was to protect America's freedom. This freedom that allowed a man like Larry Schafer to compete in the world of free enterprise. The Stealth F-117 Nighthawk, housed in nearby Edwards Air Force base, reminded Larry that to be successful, he needed to stay a step ahead of his competitors.

As the Caravan turned and headed west, Larry's eyes moved off the highway to the vast population of Joshua trees, which Larry had heard grow in only two places on earth: Israel and, of course, the Mojave desert, extending to Arizona and Nevada. Larry was no botanist, but assumed the many Joshua tree stories told by high desert customers were true. He had not seen the Joshua in Israel, but figured they were twins to the mysterious trees sprouting all around him. The unique, spiny members of the yucca family inspired a national park in Twenty-Nine Palms and are sometimes described as desert palms.

Perennially green, Joshua trees can endure dry, scorching summer days. They are equally adept at coping with frigid winter nights, their branches adorned with snowflakes from desert storms. In the spring, wildflowers surround the Joshua, seemingly, as a celebration to survival. There were many days when Larry felt just like a Joshua tree: bull doggedly surviving in the industrial sales rep business.

Dusty towns like Victorville, Palmdale, and Lancaster are typical high desert boom towns that are far more bust than boom. They are Southern California's sun baked and windblown afterthoughts, never lumped together with the sprawling, wall-to-wall aberration of crammed cities referred to as Greater Los Angeles. To the L.A. masses, towns like Lancaster are not even distant cousins.

No, the high desert is not Los Angeles and the grassroots of the high desert population is happy about that because they want no part of the traffic, smog, or frantic pace. They refer to people 2,000 feet below them, in Greater Los Angeles, as 'flatlanders'. Newcomers to the high desert, typically flatlanders, move to the high desert for amazingly affordable homes on large cheap lots, and then commute up and down long winding passes to L.A. to toil in the jobs that they wished were closer to home.

Larry's mind ricocheted from one random thought to another. He now wondered why John Brown made Lancaster the corporate headquarters for Quantum Supply. As he worked his way to the fast lane, he rebutted his own question. Money! Like a spiritual calling, John followed the end of the rainbow to the pot of gold rumored to be hidden in Lancaster. He spent every day of his life in search of it.

Driving to Valencia required Larry to travel the dichotomy of going south on the 14 and then north on Interstate 5. On the map this route resembles the "V" shaped graph of the Dow Jones Industrials after a bullish day. Larry would drive down the back leg of the letter "V" and up the front of it. Valencia was just west of Lancaster, but there was no easily traveled east-west route that connected the two towns. He shook his head and mumbled to himself, "You just can't get there from here!"

Not surprisingly, the mobile phone rang. "How do you like that Caravan?"

"Not too bad, Frank. I'm running it hard and long!"

"Larry, the factory tells me you're pestering them about the RP Supply order."

"That's true."

"Don't be too hard on the girls on the order desk. The factory is just now gearing up production for California compliant product. Do you know what Fabricio Merano says about the state you and I both live in?"

"The state of confusion?"

"Very funny, Larry."

"Who the heck is Fabricio Merano?"

"Larry you have lots to learn. He's the president of Independence Water Heaters."

"The only way I would know that tidbit is for you to tell me. It proves you're withholding valuable information from me."

"Are you through yet, Larry?"

"With what?"

"With driving me to an early grave!"

"So what does Mr. Merano have to say about Ronald Reagan's favorite state?"

"That since we do everything different in California, we have become the 'People's Republic of California'. Did you know that we are the only state that requires low NOx product?"

"What's that?"

"California requires factories to manufacture water heaters that reduce the number of nitrogen oxide particulates they emit into the air."

"Why?"

"Because they contribute to smog."

"Water heaters cause smog?"

"You're a slow learner, Larry, but you're starting to catch on."

"I'm in Lancaster. There's no smog here."

"That brings up a good point. Lancaster doesn't require California product and neither does Ventura or San Diego."

"So some parts of California don't require California product? That doesn't make any sense."

"There you go again."

"I know, I'm applying logic to the water heater business. I get it. Because the People's Republic of California requires low NOx heaters, the factory can't ship my order because it's shipping to Riverside instead of Lancaster."

"Well, not yet, Larry. The factory is doing its best to get your order on the production schedule."

"So I sold product that we can't make!"

"We can make it, but your customers need to be patient."

"Red's not that patient. He gave me an ear full this morning. Russ Petersen is not that patient either. Maybe I should stop selling until the factory figures out how to produce and ship People's Republic of California product."

"Larry, don't stop selling until I tell you."

"Does that mean that you're going to get my RP order shipped?"

"Yes, Larry, I'm working on it. Why do I always regret calling you?"

"I don't know Frank, but I'm on my way to 'Water Heaters For Less' to sell some more and find out about stickers."

"What?"

"Stickers! I don't understand it either, but John Brown tells me a Sicilian named Leo Rodini is going to talk to me about stickers."

"Larry, you are torturing my brain."

"Your brain is tortured? I just spent an hour with John Brown. I feel like I took a trip to Rome without getting a chance to make a wish at the Trevi Fountain. I was like a German kindergartener in a trigonometry class taught in Italian. My brain feels like a bowl of spaghetti. And now you call to tell me about water heater smog in the People's Republic of California."

"It's been nice talking to you, Larry. It's getting close to noon in Denver. I definitely need a martini after this conversation."

"Frank, I think it's great that you're going to have a martini. In fact, you should have two. It's a great way to celebrate the shipment of my RP Supply order into the People's Republic of California. By the way, Mr. P is expecting his truckload by next Friday."

Larry hung up the phone just in time to recalibrate his brain to transition from the southbound 14 to the northbound 5.

The phone rang again. It was Susan. "Good morning, Larry. Guess what?"

"Here we go again, what should I guess?"

"Larry! When I say guess what, I'm not really asking you to guess. I'm just saying 'guess what'. Get it?"

"So after you say 'guess what', what should I say?"

"I don't know, Larry, just don't guess. As usual you are being very difficult."

There was a silence from both sides of the phone call when Susan broke the silence, "So, guess what?"

Larry was silent.

Susan retorted, "CHC called."

"What?"

"Community Health Care, Larry."

"Oh yeah, the hall pass people."

"I'm rolling my eyes again, Larry, you just can't see me. You have an 8 o'clock appointment tomorrow with Dr. Van Slyke, a neurologist."

"A neurologist? That sounds scary. What's a neurologist?"

"They specialize in nerves."

"Nerves?"

"Yes, nerves."

"My nerves are fine unless I'm talking to John Brown about the Ray Brown special."

"What in the world is the Ray Brown special?"

"A venti latte, a cannoli, and a CD."

"This conversation is like a bad dream!"

"That's how I felt in my meeting with John Brown. My lip started twitching. I think it was a nerve problem, but thankfully, it went away. My only real problem that isn't going away is my heavy legs. It seems like there should be a doctor for that. I suppose I'll see this nerve doctor to get another hall pass. Is there such a thing as a 'heavy-leg-otologist'?"

Susan ignored Larry being Larry. "By the way, Mary and I just had coffee together."

"Did you add a spoon full of sugar to make you sweet and a splash of milk to make you smile?"

"No, Larry. Because I'm married to you, I don't need those artificial additives to make me happy."

"Ah, that is so, so sweet! Okay! I get it. You had a Bailey's coffee."

"You're becoming a better guesser. Anyway Larry, Mary says that you need to ship Red some water heaters. Evidently your water heaters are making everybody crazy!"

"I'm working on this issue with Frank."

"What did he say?"

"He said they'll ship the order as soon as they figure out how to make them."

"That doesn't sound promising Larry. I'll remind you that I advised you to take the job in the wholesale business working for the pencil breaker."

"I know…I know. I'll figure it out. Tell Mary to tell Red I'm definitely working on it. Evidently, the problem is that we now live in the People's Republic of California?"

"What?"

"Oh, never mind, it's a long story."

"After we figure out why your legs are heavy, we need to find out how to unscramble the eggs in your head. And Larry, don't forget!"

"Don't forget what?"

"Larry! Don't forget about your appointment tomorrow at 8 AM."

"Okay, okay. I'll be there. I'll talk to you later."

The exhausting conversation took Larry and his Caravan five miles past his turnoff. He exited and headed back south on the 5 and then carefully followed his hand written instructions. He parked in front of the address. There was no office, no warehouse and not a sign of water heaters anywhere. John said that 'Water Heaters For Less' bought more water heaters than any contractor he knew. Something had gone awry! The address John had provided led Larry to a ranch style home, not a business. He double checked everything, scratched his head and called Quantum Supply. "John, I'm parked in front of a house and need to verify the address."

"Is it a yellow house with a white split rail fence around it?"

"Yes."

"Sounds like you found it, Larry. Good work. I hope nobody followed you."

"Followed me?"

"Yes."

"Does this Sicilian deal in drugs or water heaters?"

"Larry, just remember, you promised me that we would keep Leo a secret."

"Hang on, John."

A tall thin man approached Larry's van. His dark, curly hair, partially untucked tee shirt, and easy going stride were married to a no nonsense expression on his face. He approached Larry and rapped on the window.

Larry balanced confusion inside and outside of his van, then rolled down the window. "You must be Leo."

"And you must be the water heater guy."

"Yes I am."

"Good, follow me and we'll grab some breakfast."

As Leo walked toward his truck, Larry returned to his conversation with John. "Okay, John, we're all set. I'm following Leo to a restaurant."

"That's a good start Larry. Now you'll enter the untapped world of water heater stickers. Call me when you're through!"

"Yes sir."

"And Larry!"

"Yes sir!"

"Don't talk to anyone about the secrets that Leo will reveal."

Larry mumbled to himself, "Why in the world did that conversation with John feel exactly like my previous conversations with Frank and Susan?"

During Larry's moment of head scratching silence, John commented once more, "Did you hear me, Larry. Keep this secret a secret and call me after breakfast!"

Five minutes later, Leo's truck pulled into Flappy Jack's, a small diner that looked like a place Larry would frequent. In the parking lot, the two men shook hands and then walked into a crowded, noisy chaos that reminded Larry of the Flier's Café. Because he had a non-threatening way about him, plumbers were just as comfortable around Larry as Larry was around them. He had a way of selling that never made the customer feel like he was being sold.

After ordering coffee, Larry started the ball rolling. "So Leo, John is driving me crazy about these stickers that, apparently, are hotter than the water inside of my heaters."

Leo smiled. "John makes it sound intriguing, doesn't he? The truth of the matter is that my idea is very simple, but it works."

Leo pulled a sticker out of the back pocket of his jeans. "Here you are, this is the magic sticker."

Larry studied the bright red sticker and looked up with a smile, "So you send this to homeowners with the idea that they are going to stick it on their water heater."

Leo's eyes lit up like fireworks on the fourth of July. "You got it, Larry. The instructions to shut off the water and gas valves are apparently good enough emergency tips that people actually take the time to put the sticker on their water heater."

Larry beamed excitedly. "And then, of course, when their water heater leaks and they've followed your instructions, they call you. I love it!"

"You're a quick study."

"So, Leo, I know there's a wrinkle in here. How can I help you?"

"A major ad campaign where we mail 25,000 stickers is expensive. I'm looking for a partner in my sticker program. What's the name of your water heaters again?"

"Independence."

"Okay. In exchange for your sponsorship, I advertise Independence Water Heaters on the sticker as the brand we install, and I make a deal with you that we will buy your product exclusively. Of course, your price has to be competitive and you need to manufacture a product we will be proud to install. I'm sure you understand!"

Larry had numbers tumbling around in his head like popcorn in a popper. "So, what do you think is the return on the investment? It seems to me that you might have to wait ten to twelve years for heaters to leak."

"Not really. I've done the math. There's a high probability of getting a call in 1 to 1,000 days. You see, I do research to identify particular zip codes where houses were built 8-10 years earlier. Those houses are likely to have heaters ready to leak. What do you think, Larry?"

"I think I like it Leo. In fact, I think I love it. How many water heaters a year do you think you'll replace with this program?"

"Maybe 5,000. Maybe more. It all depends on how much money you contribute. The more you kick in, the more stickers I can afford to mail."

"But Leo, where's your warehouse to store all of these water heaters you sell and install?"

"I don't have one. I drop containers convenient to the areas I'm targeting. My men pull product out of those storage units."

"That sounds smart. Who would you say is your biggest competitor?"

"Actually I would say the big box home improvement stores. Does your water heater offer any features that would help my phone sales people close a sale with a home owner calling our shop?"

"Well, yes. We have a self-cleaning design we call the Tornado, which prevents sediment in the tank from settling. It will make the water heater perform better for longer."

Because Leo was more salesman than plumber he was genuinely excited, "Wow!"

"Plus, our heater is not available in retail stores!"

"That's a good hook Larry. If we make a deal, you'll need to come in and train my people."

"That's easy enough."

Leo the water heater replacement king and Larry the rookie water heater salesman, finished their flapjacks, the specialty of the house, and laughed about Leo's specialty, the sticker campaign.

Larry was as happy as a dot that just got connected. "Let me go to work on this, Leo. I love what you're doing, and I think that just maybe, I can convince the Italians that run Independence Water Heaters that your sticker proposition will be a beautiful partnership for all of us. I'll get back to you."

As the men shook hands, Leo commented, "You have a unique stride."

"Yeah, that's why my contractor friends call me Ratchet-Ass. Actually, my nickname has now been shortened to Ratchet."

"Okay, I think perhaps I'll just call you Larry. Is that okay?"

"My wife Susan would prefer that."

"Good enough. It's always good to align yourself with the spouse of your business partner."

Leo and Larry had just completed the opening round of a

relationship that might pay long-term dividends. Larry fired up the Caravan and made some notes in his planner. There was still time to make it to Ventura. "Steve, this is Larry."

"Oh, so you finally decided to call me. I can't believe that it's that easy for you to forget your old friends."

"I promise to make it up to you. How about lunch today?"

"Let me think about that. You know I have a very busy schedule and I can't just drop everything because at the last second an old friend re-surfaces."

Larry pushed aside Steve's sarcastic remark, brushing it off as if it was yet another thorny comment from Red or Frank. "Steve, I'm in Valencia. I'll be there in an hour. Please call Big Ben and have him join us. I'll meet you at Johnny's Beach Bungalow at about 11:30. "

"If I'm not there, Larry, start the meeting without me."

Larry ignored Steve's comment. "See you in a bit."

As Larry transitioned from Interstate 5 to Route 126, his phone rang. It was John Brown, "I thought you were going to call me."

"Sorry, John, I was on the phone."

"I sure hope you didn't tell anybody about our sticker secret."

"No, no. I wouldn't do that. The meeting with Leo went pretty well. I need to talk to Frank to see how the factory feels about it."

"When you talk to your Italian friend, remind him that I'm Italian and that I deserve the kind of deal the big guys get. Remember, if it wasn't for me, you wouldn't know anything about stickers."

"I understand, John. You want the Ray Brown special: a venti latte, a cannoli, and a free CD. I'm hot on the trail. I'll definitely get back to you."

As Larry proceeded west on Highway 126, his phone rang yet again. The new mobile phone was getting lots of action. It was Red. "Ratchet, where in the hell are my damned water heaters?"

"Hi, Red, it sure is great hearing from you. I don't think we've talked since early this morning. I'm on my way to Johnny's Beach Bungalow. You ought to meet me there for some fish and chips."

"You really should run for political office, Ratchet. You have a way of spreading bullshit that doesn't even stink."

"I talked to Frank about the RP Supply order that has your heaters on it. He told me to be patient because the order was just placed yesterday. I told him that patience wasn't one of your virtues. I was just about to call him again when you called."

"That sounds like more Ratchet BS. And no, I'm not driving all the way to Ventura to watch you fill the back of my pickup with the truckloads of manure you're spreading. You know, Ratchet, I'm trying to meet the truck halfway, but you sure as hell make it hard."

"See you, Red. I'm on it."

Larry hung up the phone. His attempt to disarm Red with a mixture of confidence and humor worked this time but if he didn't pin down a ship date, the next conversation was sure to be different.

The Riverside phone number of RP Supply popped up. "This is Russ Petersen!"

"Hello, Mr. P."

"Why would I place a second order with you, if I can't get the first one?"

"I understand. Red just called me as well. The factory is gearing up for low NOx production as we speak. I will call you right after I talk to Frank Caparelli. I already told him the urgency of getting your order shipped."

"Larry, I will remind you that my previous water heater source is out of business. That means I'm relying on my new supplier. If you can't keep me in the water heater business, I will need to find a more reliable factory."

"I understand. I'll be in your office tomorrow at seven. Will that be okay?"

"You don't have to do that, Larry, but I really need the factory to step up to the plate. Is that clear?"

"Yes sir. I'll see you in the morning."

While stopped at a red light in Fillmore, the non-stop phone rang once again. "Good news, Larry. Your RP Supply order is scheduled to arrive in Riverside next Thursday."

"Are the water heaters legal to install in the Republic of California?"

"Yes, the first production run will occur in a couple days. The factory will have the trailer picked up by team drivers who will work around the clock to insure a prompt delivery. RP will get a call when the load is 24 hours away."

"Thank you very much! One more second, Frank."

"The meter's running. Make it quick."

"Well, through our clever friend John Brown, I have a sticker proposition for you."

"All your propositions are sticky, Larry."

"No, Frank, a sticker proposition. But it may also be a bit sticky."

"What in the hell are you talking about."

Larry proceeded to explain the Leo Rodini proposal and the Ray Brown special. Frank was in the Colorado Rockies trying to make sense of a German who knew very little about the water heater business, but was an expert at driving him crazy.

"Frank, you have no idea what it's like negotiating with an Italian who has the ability to convert cannoli cream into cash and a Sicilian who is armed with a truckload of stickers and attacks the water heater business with a double reverse squeeze."

"Larry, you never, ever cease to amaze me. Put all of that in writing and fax it to me. I need to get my head wrapped around something that is totally illogical and has an excellent chance of causing me to lose whatever is left of my mind."

Larry just couldn't resist, "Frank, you just did it!"

"I did what?"

"You just broke your own rule. You're applying logic to the water heater business."

"Larry, your unrelenting pounding on my head with your ratchet-like sledge hammer will be the demise of me. When I met you, I was six foot four. Because of you, and solely because of you, I now stand five foot eight!"

CHAPTER 18

"Pierpont Bay"

As Larry hung up his ever so popular mobile phone, he thought about his friendship with Frank and how thankful he was that his longtime pal had engineered a plan that made Larry the benefactor of a Caravan, mobile phone, and a potential source of income: a water heater line that would provide an opportunity to earn the commissions he needed to pay his bills. Then there was Frank's ranting. Larry had heard his comment about being pounded to his five foot eight size hundreds of times. The story was always told as if it was the very first time it had been uttered: with a mixture of frustration and over the top emotion. Larry and Frank were like a duet: each playing instruments that were slightly out of tune, but managing to stay on the same sheet of music, creating, together, a unique symphonic masterpiece.

It was time for a pit stop. The Caravan's tank was empty and Larry's bladder was full. He sighed, pried open the Caravan door, and took two steps towards the gas pump. As he pulled out his wallet to retrieve his American Express card, his mind attempted to harness the ever multiplying array of unconnected dots flying around inside his head. As it is when the mind is occupied with connecting dots and the immediate task is to simply pull a credit card from the pocket of a wallet, Larry fumbled the green card and watched it fall to the ground. A one word comment followed, "Damn!"

As he bent over to pick it up, a shockwave ran from his lower back to the cavity of unconnected dots, propped squarely on his shoulders. The pain was all too familiar. He had first experienced it in college and then dealt with it, on and off, the rest of his life. An unforgettable episode occurred in Cleveland, in the early eighties, when he slipped on a patch of black ice. Over the years, he had many other relapses of the sharp, jabbing jolts that had the impact of a knockout punch. Larry often wondered how pain levels so high on the Richter scale could be caused by the pinching of a minuscule nerve in the spinal region of a compromised back.

Larry pulled his body upright like a giant crane methodically lifting a car in a wrecking yard. Now standing somewhat erect, he filled the Caravan's thirsty tank and then slowly made his way to the restroom. The steps were a combination of a sideways slide and slow, excruciating steps. He could feel his upper torso being tugged to his right. When Larry dragged that leg on the golf course, Frank would remark, "Hit the ball, drag Larry."

As Larry pried open the door marked 'MEN' he was greeted by the repulsive stench of urine. Since the light in the restroom had burned out long ago, Larry left the door ajar. Cryptic graffiti characters intimidatingly sprang from the walls at him, triggering an impulsive, painful, stiffening of his neck and back. His eyes, already wide open, suddenly beamed like headlights. Piles of crumpled paper towels and a menagerie of beer cans were strewn on a floor, which had part of its vinyl pulled off the concrete.

Larry was grateful there was a urinal because the toilet was one deposit away from overflowing. The white porcelain of the wash sink had turned to various shades of brown. To punctuate its need for maintenance, a rusty faucet tap rhythmically leaked steady drops. Larry stood at the urinal which double-teamed as a cigarette butt disposal site.

He squirmed to posture himself in a position that would strike a compromise between pain and necessity. Completing the job, he zipped his pants and turned, making sure not to slip on the remnants of glass that had splashed on the floor from the cracked mirror.

After gingerly dragging himself out the door, Larry heaved a sigh and sarcastically commented under his breath, "Life on the road is filled with glamour. If by some miracle I'm blessed with even more pampering, I'll feel just like a movie star!"

He opened the door of the Caravan. Now a new challenge presented itself: maneuvering his body into a position that would allow him to sit behind the wheel. After a series of slow motion contortions, he finally situated his body and mumbled to himself, "Thanks, Frank, I don't think I could have gotten into my old Astro!" He wildly dreamed that the muscles in his back would loosen in route to Ventura, but he feared his situation would get worse before it got better.

Larry dialed his chiropractor, Dr. David in Riverside. Since he was a frequent visitor, Larry knew everyone in the office. "Hi Carol, this is Larry Schafer, I desperately need an appointment. What's the latest time available to see the doctor today?"

"I can squeeze you in at 5 o'clock."

"Perfect! I'll be coming back from Ventura. If the traffic cooperates, I should be there by five."

"Don't worry about it Larry, I'll alert Dr. David. I'm sure it won't be a problem if you run a bit late. Are you in spasm?"

"Oh yes! I feel like an electrician who hit a hot wire by mistake!"

"Oh my. You be careful, Larry. We'll see you at about five."

Larry put the Caravan in drive and continued his trip west on highway 126. He inhaled deeply and dialed Susan. "Hi"

"How's your day?"

"Lovely! I'm calling to tell you that I threw out my back."

"Oh my goodness, Larry, where are you?"

"Fillmore. I just passed one of our favorite spots, the fish hatchery."

"Are you okay?"

"In this day of adventures, I messed up my back bending over at a gas station, but was lucky to get in and out of a creepy restroom alive!"

"Oh dear, I guess that's good news, but I'm not sure!"

"I'm having a great day. Lots of good stuff. I won't allow my screwed up back to get me down."

"Larry, maybe I should pick you up. I don't like the trail you're on."

"Thank you, but there's no way I would ever be able to contort my body into the Corvette. Anyway, I would still need to get my car home. I'll be okay, I'll head back after my lunch with Steve and Big Ben. I have a 5 o'clock appointment with Dr. David."

"You worry me, Larry!"

"I didn't call you to make you worry. I just thought you should know."

"Shouldn't you skip your Ventura calls and head back now?"

"Yes, I really should, but I promised Steve I'd see him today."

"You are such a hard head, Larry. Be careful. I love you."

After driving about a mile, Larry thought about a technique that Dr. David had taught him. It was a longshot but if it worked, it would realign his tweaked vertebrae and relieve some of the pain, but it would require carpeting. He drove past fireworks vendors, fast food restaurants and strip malls before spotting a ray of hope: a Chrysler dealership that advertised a red carpet special. Larry hoped that, since he drove a Dodge, the car dealer might be sympathetic. He again went through the torturous exercise of getting his body out of the front seat. Finally he stood erect and stretched. He then arched his torso backwards to the max. He repeated that routine over and over again until he finally felt a smidgeon of relief. After taking three deep breaths, Larry hobbled gingerly into the showroom where he was immediately greeted by a salesman, "Hey there friend, my name's Fred Smiley. What's your name?"

Larry was painfully polite. "Ratchet."

"Okay Mr. Ratchet, are you here to trade in your Caravan for something a bit more sporty?"

Larry arched his back once more before replying, "Actually no, but I would like to borrow some of your carpet, perhaps in the corner, out of harm's way. You may have noticed I'm walking a bit crooked."

"Well, Mr. Ratchet, I did notice, but I've found that embarrassing customers can hinder the closing of a car deal. I'm not sure what you'll be doing in that corner, but I guess it's okay provided you keep your pants on."

"Thanks, Fred. I promise I'll be no bother."

Larry made his way to the corner of the showroom and slowly lowered his body to the red, not so plush, carpet. As he squirmed to a position that laid him flat on his back, he thought about the highs and lows of three unforgettable days. The mountains of hope had been high and the valleys of despair had been low. And now, here he was in the tiny corner of a five signal town hoping that magically he would find, with a little luck, the strength to crawl out of yet another deep valley. In the first part of the routine, he alternated a series of relaxing breathing exercises with stretching. He then rolled himself into a ball, arms clasped around his lower legs; rocking to and fro like a rocking chair, pivoting on his vertebrae.

Meanwhile, Fred Smiley had recruited everyone at the dealership to watch the stranger rock back and forth on his spine. There was a combination of pointing, laughing, and head shaking. The cute, compassionate receptionist had to be restrained from providing assistance to Larry, who was unaware of the spectacle he had made of himself.

While Larry's routine was repeated over and over again, it became obvious that, thankfully, the pain was subsiding. The tight knot in his lower back was miraculously loosening a bit. Larry spent about fifteen minutes on the floor of the dealership in relative oblivion. He had no idea that he had provided entertainment for the staff, but when he stopped the rocking, stretched, and slowly raised his body up from the floor, he received a round of applause. Larry grinned, slowly made his way out the front door, and commented, "Thanks guys, I really appreciate the red carpet treatment."

Fred Smiley bid Larry farewell. "Let us know when you are interested in trading in that Caravan, Mr. Ratchet."

The receptionist could not resist asking Larry, "Are you new in town?"

Larry made no reply to either comment, instead concentrating on the task before him, rhythmically matching each step with slow, deep breaths. He had done the ball rocking exercise many times, but never with this great a result. The process of getting into the Caravan was now much easier. He started the engine, smiled, and drove about a half mile before pulling into a drugstore. A full court press was in order. Perhaps pain relievers would also help. He bought a package of Advil and a bottle of water. He thought about taking four tablets, but stuck with three. Down the hatch they went, hopefully routed to the source of the pain. Life on the road was always an adventure, but as usual, Larry was elevating the experience to a new level.

Back on Route 126, feeling a little bit better and determined to make it through the day, Larry refocused on the job at hand. Oh, those darn dots. He then mumbled to himself, "Damn, I need to call Red and Mr. P."

As Larry drove through Santa Paula, he called RP Supply. "Hi, Marsha, is Russ already on the golf course?"

"It's eleven o'clock Larry. What do you think?"

"I think I missed him. I was just hoping that maybe I'd get lucky."

"So talking to me isn't lucky enough?"

"Okay, you're right. I'll see you in the morning on the early side."

"Just make sure the screws in your head are tightened before you see Mr. P."

"Got it."

Larry hung up and dialed Red's private office number. "Do you miss me?"

"You better have good news Ratchet!"

"Well, I do, after the red carpet treatment in Fillmore I feel much better."

"As usual, you're making as much sense as a plumber pretending to be an electrician."

"Oh, sorry. Since I don't want you to quit buying a product that you don't even have, I threw myself to the mercy of the court."

"Did the judge decide to hang your Ratchet-Ass or ship me my heaters?"

"Because the factory has figured out how to make smog-friendly heaters, they're shipping the order."

"Ratchet, I'm not sure what in the hell you just said, but it sounds like you got lucky."

"That's what Marsha just told me when I called to talk to Russ Petersen, but missed him."

"How does an English major consistently say things that I can't understand any more than Greek or Chinese?"

"Practice, I think. Don't forget that Socrates was from Greece."

"You are stinking killing me, Ratchet!"

"I'll be thinking about you when I'm having fish and chips at Johnny's Beach Bungalow. I'm just about in Ventura now. It's a bit foggy, my back is feeling better, and its 67 degrees."

"Thanks Ratchet. Let me give you the forecast here. It's so hot that I could fry your ratchet ass on the sidewalk and slice it into baloney."

Because Larry was used to Red slamming the phone on him, he brushed off the abrupt ending to their conversation. After regrouping, Larry came to the realization that in addition to making him more efficient, his mobile phone was providing a diversion: taking his mind off of his agonizing pain. Additionally, the Advil seemed to be performing a bit of magic. He would know more when he got to Johnny's, but so far so good. Larry turned onto Seaward Avenue and headed west. Johnny's was conveniently located at the end of Seaward, where pavement meets sand.

After three trips up and down an eclectic stretch of beach businesses, Larry finally found a parking spot. It was designated for one hour parking, but he decided to take a chance. He slowly wrenched himself out of his seat and ever so slowly stretched. He felt a little pain, but not the sharp pain he had first experienced. Miraculously, the combination of the red carpet special and Advil were providing at least a little bit of relief.

Moments later…Larry, salt air, and Johnny's Beach Bungalow were reunited while unconnected dots were swept into a corner. He walked through the door and was immediately greeted by a smiling Big Ben and Steve, who pretended to be angry, but couldn't quite hide the joy he felt when he saw his prized pupil approach the table. "You're walking a little gingerly."

Larry shook his head and grinned, "I'm not sure how I made it here, but somehow, I did!"

During the course of Larry's condensed version of his ride from Valencia to Ventura, the friends stayed with tradition: all ordering the fish and chips.

Big Ben gazed at the shoreline and the Channel Islands beyond. "I remember the time you got tangled up with a sting ray while body surfing, but two hours later, you still helped me slap in a 75 gallon heater.

It's good to see you haven't lost your toughness."

Steve interjected, "There's nothing in the world harder than Larry's head."

The men all laughed.

Ben continued, "You know what? If a guy can't be happy here at the beach, he's just not gonna find happiness anywhere."

Steve, an avid reader of historic books, piped in, "Did you guys know that in 1542 Juan Rodriguez Cabrillo was anchored right here in Pierpont Bay?"

Larry injected a dose of Larry being Larry, "Did he come to shore and have the fish and chips here at Johnny's Beach Bungalow?"

Ben laughed robustly while Steve rolled his eyes. A silent interval followed like the calm between waves in a set. Steve then prompted Larry, "So tell me about these new water heaters."

"You mean the ones that you're going to start buying?"

Ben sat quietly as Steve sent a flare across the Pierpont waterfront.

"I make it a habit of not supporting products that lack consistent representation."

"Okay, Steve, I get the message, but I'm hoping you'll cut me just a little bit of slack. Once I get the ball rolling and can hire some help, I'll be able to see you more often, but right now, it's a little tough."

Ben chimed in, "Don't take Steve seriously, he already told me he's going to support you, provided you give him the kind of prices he needs to sell me the heaters cheap. Really cheap!"

Larry took a bite of his fish and dipped a French fry into his tub of ketchup. "Let me throw something on the table."

Steve did not miss the opportunity, "Are you going to toss it at my tub of tartar sauce?"

"Even better, Steve. I'll get you in line to buy the hottest brand of heaters on the market while at the same time letting you gobble up the Cabrillo special for making the change to the first self-cleaning water heater on the market."

Big Ben and Steve looked puzzled, shook their heads and

simultaneously exclaimed, "What?"

"Steve, you just told us the story about Juan Rodriguez Cabrillo. The Cabrillo special will include a reliable compass, a pocket watch with a gold chain, and of course, a bottle of rum. You should also note that my product is American-made, American-owned, and is not available in retail stores."

Steve took a sip of his cola before replying, "Larry, is it the combination of Advil and root beer that's strangling your ability to think straight?"

"Independence has a standard rebate program which they evidently don't use. Every time I share it, customers laugh at me."

"So you substituted a program you just made up for the one the factory doesn't use?"

"Exactly!"

"Okay, Larry. Once you translate your Cabrillo special into English and put it in writing, I'll look at it. Do you have a printed price sheet?"

Larry handed the price sheet to Steve, who quickly handed it to Ben.

"Larry wants me to pay more for heaters than what I charge you."

"Steve, that's just our price sheet, we don't really charge those prices, that's where the Cabrillo special comes in."

Steve looked at Big Ben again. "See what I'm dealing with Ben? Because you helped me teach Larry the plumbing business, you just want to support him, unconditionally. I understand that, but just remember that Larry is a smooth salesman. Unfortunately, he learned that from me. He smiles, asks lots of questions, and then assembles a sales strategy while we're sorting through reams of Larry fairy tales. He's like a guy creating a masterpiece with jigsaw puzzle pieces floating in his head."

Ben smiled and looked at Larry. "How do you make your water heater self-cleaning?"

"With the 'Tornado'. The dip tube creates a tornado in the tank that moves sediment around instead of letting it turn into crud. Tank crud makes it hard for the burner to heat the water, which in turn makes it less efficient. The Tornado keeps crud out of the tank."

Steve jumped in, "Damn it, Larry, quit making stuff up!"

"It's a fact! An absolute fact! As soon as I get my literature shipment, I'll show you the brochure. You guys ought to be able to sell these heaters at a higher price."

"So let me see if I have this right, Larry. You want me to buy your water heaters even though you have no set pricing, no brochures and a program you just pulled out of a seashell?"

"Our pricing will be set. I'm just not finished setting it up."

Steve turned to Ben, "What do you think Ben?"

"I like the Tornado and I like the idea that Larry is not selling them to the big box stores. Plus, I'm an American, so I love product made in this country."

Larry grabbed the bill and responded, "Thanks, Ben. I really appreciate that. Steve, is there any chance I can swing by the shop real quick to fax my boss a memo?"

"First off, Larry, hand me that check. It's my treat. Secondly, in your heart tugging story about the red carpet special you told me you had a chiropractor's appointment in Riverside tonight. Don't you think you should hit the road?"

"Yes, but it seems like everyone I talk to needs responses from me on every detail of every program a little quicker than right away."

"There you go again, Larry! And by the way, I'm low on water heaters and need to order, so you really need to get me something in writing by tomorrow. One more piece of business. Do your commercial heaters have flue dampers?"

"Well, unfortunately, it sounds like they are now required by law."

"I'm going to take that as a 'yes'! Flue dampers are causing my customers lots of grief. They're a callback nightmare!"

"What's the problem with them?"

"Just about every commercial water heater we send to a job needs to have the damper fixed or replaced with parts and spare dampers we don't have!"

Larry shook his head. "Now you're starting to sound like me. Either that, or I'm sounding like you. Anyway, I'll send out a care package with plenty of spare dampers and parts. Let's call it insurance. I'm betting my product will work better than the stuff you're buying, but just in case there's a problem, you'll be covered."

Steve turned to Big Ben, "Do you think Larry is a water heater rep or an insurance salesman?"

Ben retorted in his easy, happy way, "Well, Steve, it kind of looks like he's our new water heater supplier."

Steve added closure, "Not until he translates the Cabrillo special!"

Larry made his way back to the Caravan. Because his back was tightening, he walked much like the tin man in the Wizard of Oz. Was the Advil wearing off or was his body merely screaming to be positioned horizontally after a long, punishing day? As he headed down Seaward Ave. and turned left on Thompson Blvd., he thought to himself that, thankfully, everything in Ventura is five minutes away. Dick's Plumbing Wholesale was no different.

Larry pulled into Dick's parking lot, grinning ear to ear. At that very moment, being a rookie in the water heater business was not a bad gig. No, he wasn't making any money, but the events of the first two days rekindled hope, which fueled his desire to succeed. His back? It would get relief a little bit later when he was in the hands of Dr. David.

Whenever Larry walked through the front door of Dick's, he felt like the prince at a homecoming dance. His favorite was Steve's wife, Lindsay. She wore a perpetual smile and was always positive. She was small in stature, but gifted with a huge heart. She invariably put everyone else's needs ahead of her own. No matter how busy, she always went out of her way to be amazingly accommodating. A hug from Lindsay made Larry forget about the unconnected dots in his head and the pain in his back.

After greeting everyone else, he headed to the back office, grabbed a piece of Dick's stationary, and wrote up the proposals for Quantum Supply, 'Water Heater's For Less', and now Dick's. He requested programs for Red and Big Ben that provided no-charge product for model homes. He then sent the fax to Frank and headed toward the showroom where Steve was working his magic: consulting with a contractor needing whirlpool tubs for a remodel project. Larry squeezed in a quick handshake. "Thanks a million, Steve, I'm working on your pricing and program. I just sent the memo to Frank. I'll have something to you very quickly."

"Take care of that back, Larry, and give Susan a hug for me. It would be nice if you brought her up here with you. That would dilute the irritation of Larry being Larry. If you play your cards right, Lindsay might even perform some kitchen magic. How does pork roast and dumplings sound?"

CHAPTER 19

"Doctor David"

It was two o'clock. Larry's return to Riverside for his 5 PM appointment, in rush hour traffic, would be dicey but possible. As he headed south on the 101 and crossed his fingers, his phone rang. It was Susan. "How's it going?"

"I'm hanging in there. With a little luck, I'll arrive to Dr. David's office on time. I'm hoping to be home at about 6:30. How's your day been?"

"Worrisome! I have two huge problem children. One of them is the moratorium. Guess who the other one is?"

"Do you really want me to guess? You know I'm not too good at the guessing game."

"No Larry, don't guess because you know exactly what to guess."

"Oh, I get it, if I know what to guess I shouldn't guess, but if I don't know what to guess, I should guess. Is that right?"

"No, Larry, you really don't get it. It all depends on the situation."

"I don't get it."

"That's exactly what I just said. You don't get it. But never mind, because you'll probably never get it. So guess what?"

Larry was confused, but opted to stay silent."

"I'm preparing a dinner that might make your back feel better."

"Susan's kitchen must be in full swing."

"Of course!"

"Another one of your creative masterpieces!"

"It's not a Rembrandt, but it is meat loaf!"

"I would have never guessed it was meat loaf night."

"That's why I didn't let you guess."

"I love meatloaf!"

"I know that. Who else would I be cooking it for? Charlie?"

"Well, I'm pretty sure that Charlie would love a piece."

"I'm sure he would. In fact, if you don't stop irritating me, Charlie might get all of it." Susan paused for a moment before continuing, "You worry me, Larry. Be careful!"

"I'll be just fine."

"Call me after you see Dr. David."

"Of course!"

Larry hung up and reoriented himself. During his conversation with Susan, his Caravan had traveled forty miles east on the 101 to Woodland Hills. The phone rang again. "Hi Larry, this is Brenda."

"Hi Brenda, it's great to hear from you."

"Thanks, Larry. I'm calling to tell you that Jimmy's office is still available. Karl told me he would like to break you into pencil pieces, but would still hire you."

"Thanks, Brenda, but I really do like being an independent rep. I love being self-reliant."

"I would think it would be lonely being independent. Think about it, Larry."

"Sorry, Brenda, I already have."

"If you keep this up, I'll start breaking your pencils as well!"

It seemed like everyone enjoyed either getting in the last word or slamming the phone down on Larry. No matter, he was now heading east on the 210. As he approached the 605 interchange, the time was 3:20, and traffic came to a halt. The phone rang. "Larry, this is Frank."

"You must have received my fax."

"I drag my tired ass and suitcase full of dirty clothes home from Denver only to be greeted by a memo from you that reads more like a mystery novel."

"So what do you think, Frank? Are you on board?"

"Since when does an explorer I learned about in the fourth grade have anything to do with water heaters?"

"You're talking about the Cabrillo program for Dick's Plumbing Supply."

"I'm glad you can keep them straight."

"In my quest to find clever sales angles, I'm letting my creative juices flow."

"Creative? You must think I'm Sherlock Holmes."

"Perhaps I should explain that the Ray Brown program is connected to the sticker program."

"And how about the Socrates Reuben Sandwich Program?"

"It's for Clarence Silverman, Silverman Plumbing!"

"And what distributor do I connect Silverman Plumbing to?

"I haven't connected that dot."

"Larry, do you understand why all of this is just a bit confusing?"

"Come on, Frank, can you help me?"

"You don't really want me to answer that, do you?"

"Seriously, Frank."

"I think we might be able to work out the programs that you submitted, but I really need to talk to the factory. I should be able to call them early tomorrow and get something back to you. How did you arrive at the numbers you proposed?"

"I took what I learned at RP and applied it to Quantum and Dick's. I then applied what I've learned from Red and applied it to 'Water Heaters For Less'. Then I scrapped our price sheet and standard program, replacing them with something that makes a little more sense. Along the way, I had some fun by naming my proposals creative names."

"And you created all this confusion and craziness in one day?"

"The model home programs for Red and Big Ben were straight forward. See, I'm looking after you!"

"Larry, you do understand that your silly names will not appear on the actual programs?"

"Why? Are you afraid that the factory will think I'm a wacko?"

"Oh no! That's a given! They figured that out very quickly. I think that became evident the very first phone call you made to the corporate office. But don't worry, they just think you are a product of a looney tunes state."

Larry ignored Frank's comment. "Thanks for the Caravan. I messed up my back today and was very grateful to have something I could get in and out of easily. If it wasn't for the new van, I'd probably still be in Fillmore. By the way, how do they charge us for use of the mobile phone?"

"By the minute. You're on a 1,000 minute plan."

"Oh my, that needs to be raised, I might be at that number already."

"Larry, I sold the factory on the idea of getting you that phone based on budgeting the carrier's maximum minute plan of 1,000 minutes."

"Are you telling me you want me in my office instead of in front of customers?"

"I'll talk to the factory. In the meanwhile, keep selling. Good sales numbers forgive a multitude of sins."

"Like talking on the phone?"

"Yes! Say good-bye to Frank! You're racking up more minutes while you're pounding me."

"But minutes spent arguing about minutes shouldn't count against my minutes."

"I think I just lost another inch. You're killing me, Larry. I need a martini."

Larry squirmed in his seat a bit. His back was talking to him, perhaps in Italian. Thankfully he would be arriving to Dr. David's office a few minutes early. He exited Central Avenue, a familiar location because it led to both his chiropractor and the German deli. Larry wiggled painfully in his seat and pulled into a very generous parking spot, which Dr. David designed so that crippled bodies like Larry's would have plenty of room to maneuver when getting in and out of their vehicles. After a treatment, it was always easier to get behind the wheel. Since he was the last patient of the day, Larry walked into an empty reception area and was immediately greeted by a sympathetic Carol. "Hang in there, Larry. Have a seat while I get your chart."

"I need to stretch a bit, so I'm going to stand."

A few minutes later, Carol opened the side door with a folder in her hand. "Let me take you back now, and we'll start you on some ultrasound."

After zig-zagging through a maze of hallways, Larry settled into his cubicle. He loosened his belt and climbed onto the treatment table, a leather apparatus that was high on firmness and function but low on comfort. Lying on his belly, his head fit onto the portion of the table designed to support a head facing straight down, while providing a cavity for breathing.

The therapist came in and started applying ultrasound to the source of the pain. On early morning appointments, the head of the device was brutally cold, but this late in the day it was at the perfect temperature. Larry could feel a soothing relief as the therapist sent ultrasound therapy deep into his back. That was followed by a vibrating massage treatment that made Larry's entire body tingle. After placing a warm towel on his back, the therapist announced, "Dr. David will be right in to see you."

Dr. David always made his presence known with a booming, happy, take charge voice, "Looks like our old friend is acting up!"

Larry relayed the story about bending over to pick up his credit card and the red carpet treatment. Dr. David's jolly laughter, as usual, hit 8.4 on the Richter scale. Doctor David began poking around Larry's lower back, asking, "How does that feel?

"Okay"

"How about this?"

"Okay"

"That means that this hurts!"

As the doctor pressed his thumb into the source of the pain, Larry exploded, "OUCH!"

The doctor calmly responded, "Yeah, that's kind of what I figured."

Dr. David kept his magical hands working on Larry's back with a series of strategic twisting, stretching, and pressure point adjustments. The treatment was a mixture of torturous pain and ecstatic relief. In the end, his back loosened and started to feel better. "Okay, Larry, no golf for a few days, and make sure you schedule a follow-up appointment."

The doctor helped Larry off the table and smiled. Larry then talked about his physical struggles walking up steps and his steep driveway. Lastly, he told Dr. David about his appointment the next morning with

Dr. Van Slyke.

The bearded doctor gave Larry every ounce of his attention: ears receptive and eyes beaming. He replied as a friend not as a doctor, "Larry, for years now I've done my best to help you feel as good as you can feel, but I'm glad you are being proactive. It's critically important that we get to the root of your issues. If you find something out tomorrow, swing by and fill me in."

Larry always felt better after visits with the good doctor, both physically and mentally. Dr. David was good medicine. As Larry headed in the direction of the ranch via Van Buren Blvd., he called Susan, "Hi."

"How's the back?"

"Much better thanks to the red carpet treatment, Advil, and Dr. David."

"Must you always speak in riddles?"

"Sorry!"

"Are you okay?"

"Yes, I'm okay. And I'll be home in a bit."

"Great, the meatloaf is just about ready."

Larry was happy to be heading home. He had departed the ranch nearly fourteen hours earlier, and was now in the wind-up phase of his wacky day that had him routed in triangular fashion through four counties. When he reached Penny Lane, he quietly celebrated. The ranch, even in its weedy condition, looked splendid. He usually stopped at the barn to check faxes in his office and say 'Hi' to Sergeant Pepper, but enough was enough. As he pulled into the driveway and parked next to Susan's classic Corvette, an excited Charlie lumbered over to greet him.

The events of the day all seemed to crash down on him. He felt like a marathon runner that collapses at the finish line. He paused to put the day into perspective and collect fragments of sanity. It was just one day; one really long day, with the promise of many more to follow. Larry tried to bend over to accept a Charlie kiss, but his body wouldn't allow it. A pat on the chocolate lab's head would need to suffice.

Larry walked through the back door to the inviting smell of Susan's kitchen. Susan smiled as she removed another one of her scrumptious specialties from the oven. For the occasion, the 'Rubber Soul' album was playing in the background. Larry loved millions of things about Susan, but near the top of the list, was her ability to create a relaxing mood with food, music, and, of course, love. Their relationship was at times combative, but, like the spices in a meatloaf, an understated mutual love was always layered in their hearts. After a quick kiss, Larry started the conversation, "So what's going on with the moratorium?"

"Are you really okay?"

"Well no, but I'm doing a lot better now than I did when I first bent over to pick up my credit card."

"What did Dr. David have to say?"

"What you and I both know: that I need to find out why my body seems to be eroding like the trail leading to the gazebo."

"It will be interesting to see what the neurologist has to say tomorrow."

Through the course of the conversation, Susan loaded up their plates with meatloaf, potatoes, and green beans. A generous scoop of gravy was the finishing touch.

Larry savored that very first taste, which was always the best. "Wow, that's good. I sure needed this! Let's hope the doctor tomorrow has some answers. But you didn't answer my question. What's going on with the moratorium?"

"Well, guess what?"

Larry didn't answer.

Susan continued, "Nothing is ever as easy as you think it's going to be. It seems that there are folks in town that believe increasing the number of housing permits will be a good thing."

Larry replied, "If a little is good then more is better."

"Yes, Larry. That is exactly what they are thinking."

Larry was quick on his feet, verbally anyway, "Don't let a few wackos interfere with common sense."

"You're right."

"At times, more can be better than a little bit, but in other cases you run the risk of creating too much supply for limited demand. It's a fine line."

Susan sighed, "You're actually making sense."

"I know that's surprising, but I like to keep you guessing."

As 'Norwegian Wood' played in the background and Charlie sat in his corner patiently waiting for leftovers, Larry thought about his roller-coaster like day. It was a day of connecting dots and adding more dots to the growing pile of items requiring attention. It was a day of good luck and bad luck; a day of pain and relief; business challenges aplenty and cleverly angled solutions.

Larry was blessed. He made friends easily and managed to keep them, even when large chunks of time separated a relationship. His address book was full of people that loved to give him a hard time. His personality attracted a steady bombardment of ball busting, but Larry was adept at dishing it back and smiling at the same time.

As for Susan, Larry knew how lucky he was. In addition to being caring and stunningly gorgeous, she fenced tenaciously with him on any topic thrown into a conversation. When he was down and vulnerable, she was tough and at the same time nurturing. Over the years they had worked themselves through challenges both small and large. In the end, they always seemed to be okay. And, there were many days that okay felt really good. Even though Larry drove her crazy, Susan loved him unconditionally. That in itself was as beautiful as a Rembrandt painting and as tasty as a ranch meatloaf dinner.

CHAPTER 20

"The Coffee Pot"

Larry slowly opened the squeaky barn door that led to the smell of hay, horse manure, and of course, Connection Sales. It would be a hot scorching summer day in the sprawling eastern belt of Southern California known as the Inland Empire. Forecasts called for Santa Ana winds to howl. Freeways would be populated with overheated cars, while seventy mile an hour wind gusts would likely push an occasional tractor trailer to its side, perilously skidding wreckage and debris across highway lanes. Highs in Lake Mathias were projected to top 100 degrees Fahrenheit.

As Larry started the coffee pot, the day's schedule tumbled around his head like the thorny tumbleweeds that would be blowing across dusty, sun-baked roads today. It was Larry's nature to focus on the *Jelly Beans in Life*, but still, sometimes it is impossible to ignore reality. There are days, it seems, that life itself can sour even the sweetest jelly beans in the bag.

It was 5 AM. Larry's plan was to be at RP Supply by 6:15 and then scurry to Community Health Services for his 8 o'clock appointment with Dr. Van Slyke. If things worked out, after his doctor appointment, he would visit some of Classic Plumbing Supply's branches to drum up interest in his lifeline: Independence Water Heaters.

His clever sales angle for Classic was bottom-up. If he was successful, the key sales people and managers at the branches would beg the corporate decision makers to bring Independence Water Heaters into their locations. He would ask smart questions designed to expose problems that Reliable Water Heater, Classic's current supplier, was having that Independence, and most importantly, Larry's service could remedy.

Larry filled his Ventura coffee mug and let the wonderful aroma enter his body through his prominent nose. As he walked to the Dutch door he made a mental note to call Frank on his way to the doctor. Although he hated to, Larry felt that he really needed to pester his mentor regarding the proposals that were faxed.

Predictably, as the upper portion of the door slowly opened, Sergeant

Pepper's big head filled the opening. Just as the Sarge was programmed to go to the open Dutch door for jelly beans, Larry was programmed to offer his four legged friend the treats.

"I'm going to the medical center today. If this doctor is worth his jelly beans, he'll identify the cause of my physical struggles and offer a remedy. That's also my aim with Classic Plumbing Supply: identify the source of any water heater pain they are experiencing and prescribe a solution."

The Sarge kicked the barnyard door in confirmation.

"Anyway, after the red carpet special and the magic hands of Dr. David, my back is feeling a little bit better, but still, if I don't move in a calculated slow motion fashion, an electrical shock wave jolts me to reality. And, to be honest, I'm getting a bit tired of this reality."

Larry stopped himself. "I'm so sorry, Sarge. I'm whining, aren't I?"

The conversation was unexpectedly interrupted by Charlie, who greeted the barn with a singular woof.

"Charlie? What the heck brings you to the barn at five in the morning?"

Charlie replied with another woof.

"I get it."

Larry pulled a handful of jelly beans from his pocket and gave them to an appreciative Charlie. The Sarge stood proud and patient, but was definitely looking for more.

Another surprise followed. "Guess what Larry? It's a family meeting!"

Larry couldn't believe it. Susan had joined the fray. After a good morning kiss, Larry beamed. "That was even sweeter than a handful of jelly beans."

"So guess what, Larry?"

Larry was puzzled, perhaps stupefied. It was summer vacation and Susan was up and dressed before the crack of dawn. And now, as he sipped his coffee, preparing for a busy day of connecting dots in his head, Susan was playing the 'guess what' game, "Did you win the lottery?"

Susan ignored Larry's comment altogether. "I'm going to your doctor appointment with you."

Larry was both bewildered and pleased all in one scrambled package. "I guess that means you're making a sales call with me. Before I go to yet another doctor and get yet another hall pass, I'm stopping at RP Supply."

"Sounds like fun, Larry. Are we going to sell something?"

Larry avoided the question. "Let me pour you a cup of coffee and then we'll sort through the incoming faxes together. Doesn't that sound like fun?"

"You always were a sweet talker. It's the result of all those jelly beans you eat, I suppose?"

Larry, followed by Susan, headed towards the fax machine while Charlie followed the Sarge into the pasture. There were rolled faxes on the desk and floor; lots of activity, to be sure. To save Larry from painfully bending over, Susan gathered the faxes on the floor and handed them to her husband. Altogether, there were eleven. Larry thumbed through them to see if there was anything really good or really bad in the pile of correspondence. The answer was no: five memos from PROH$_2$O, who had not removed Larry from their FAX list; a memo from Independence about an upcoming plant shut-down; and three orders for Larry's line of test plugs. Those orders combined might earn enough for breakfast at the Flier's.

While Susan walked outside, Larry forwarded the orders and crammed folders into his brief case. A moment later, she appeared with a big box. "Looks like the UPS man was here."

"Oh great, that's the literature I've been waiting for."

"Larry, there are six boxes here from your Italian friends. Five are marked "printed material" and one is marked 'promo'."

"Let's take a look at the promo box."

Susan opened the carton and pulled out a giant coffee machine in the shape of a water heater with Independence Water Heaters boldly imprinted. Larry grabbed it enthusiastically. "This is part of the package that a distributor gets when they become a customer. We'll give this to RP Supply this morning."

Susan looked over the prized contraption and gave her head a skeptical shake. She then opened the literature box and handed Larry an Independence Water Heater brochure touting the Tornado. "Really, Larry? Did they have to name it the Tornado? They couldn't come up with anything more creative than that? I sure hope their product is better than their marketing strategy."

"The plumbers I talk to find the Tornado very interesting."

"The name or what it does?"

"Both!"

"I guess I didn't consider the target audience."

"Red and Big Ben are intrigued by the Tornado. They think their builders will be as well."

"I stand corrected."

"The survival of Connection Sales is dependent on these water heater people being really smart."

Susan was silent and then perked right up, "Guess what, Larry?"

Larry was both speechless and exasperated.

Susan smiled. "After further review, I think I love the Tornado!"

As the Schafers drove down Penny Lane, Susan worried about their trail in life. There had been very little discussion with Larry, but it bothered her that the city council was again wrestling with the moratorium and that it would again be a hot topic at yet another town hall meeting. Mayor Sam had a quiet, relaxed, and understated confidence in front of a full house. He could speak to a crowd as if he were having a conversation in his living room. Susan, on the other hand, was always nervous but overcame her apprehension by knowing the facts and having a clear cut vision that differentiated right from wrong.

But that part of the trail could be traveled without long term consequences. The trail that she and Larry were on was altogether different. Perhaps there was nothing to worry about. Perhaps she was over reacting. Perhaps there were easy solutions for what she envisioned to be a complex challenge. She was eager to be with Larry at the doctor's office to support him. But, she also wanted to hear first-hand the truth of the matter, not a story that Larry weaved together to reassure her.

As they drove down Wood Road, a tumbleweed broadsided the Caravan, undoubtedly doing damage to the paint on the van's side. Susan commented, "It looks like our trail will be filled with surprises today."

"Welcome to my world. Life as a salesman on the road is jam-packed with detours and unscheduled stops, but there are hidden opportunities around each bend, if we can just find a clever angle. There are actually times that the opportunities are discovered after we stop looking for them."

Susan rolled her eyes. "So, Mr. Larry Shafer, president of the internationally acclaimed firm known as Connection Sales. You have the amazing ability to connect dots without even attempting to join them? The dots just fly around the universe and miraculously connect to their match?"

"I'm pretty sure we met exactly that way."

Susan shook her head and smiled. "So you are both philosopher and hopeless romantic?"

"I'm a simple salesman!"

Susan ignored Larry's deflection. "Are you sure you don't want to write a philosophical, romantic novel?"

Larry turned to the business at hand. "At RP Supply, I need to talk to Mr. Petersen about his initial Independence order that he desperately needs and persuade him to place another order."

"If I were him, I sure as heck wouldn't give you a second order when you can't ship the first one."

"If the Democrats in California didn't pass laws requiring special product for the Republic of California, RP's order would be on its way."

Larry struck a nerve in Susan that triggered an immediate response, "Oh boy, here you go again. I should have known that eventually you'd figure out a way to blame Democrats for the shortcomings of Republican businesses."

Larry pulled into RP Supply. The parking lot was full of plumbing trucks loading materials they would need for the day. "Would you like to come in with me on this sales call, or wait in the van?"

"Do they have coffee here?"

"Well, kind of. It's supply house coffee. Supply house coffee is only considered coffee in the loosest definition of the word."

"Sounds wonderful. I think I'll join you."

As Larry and Susan headed to the counter sales entrance, Red was walking out holding a bag of plumbing supplies he had just purchased. After greeting Susan with a big hug he turned to Larry, "Ratchet, I hear you have a doctor appointment today."

"As a matter of fact, I do."

"Then what in the hell are you doing here?"

Larry grinned and replied, "I came by for some great supply house coffee."

"Yeah, right."

Larry continued, "Actually, I'm here to talk to Russ about water heaters."

Larry's comment invited more needling, "I didn't know you sold water heaters. I've never seen one."

Larry acted annoyed, something he was not too good at. "Why are you here pestering me instead of enjoying breakfast at the Flier's?"

"I also came here for the worst coffee in the western world. Make sure you call me after talking to the doctor about being a Ratchet-Ass. And in your spare time, it would be really nice if you could get some water heaters in here so I can buy them."

Since Larry was accustomed to punishment, he just stood there, accepting the abuse with a smile.

Red turned to Susan, "I'm so glad that Larry is your responsibility and not mine!"

As Larry and Susan walked into the counter area, loaded with plumbers ordering material, Larry took charge. "Let's get that coffee you've been yearning to have."

The Styrofoam cups at the coffee station only held enough brew to chase down one of the greasy donuts from the jumbo box invitingly displayed next to the coffee. The adjacent city counter was crammed with sweaty bodies and smelly parts that plumbers needed to replace.

Susan looked up to see a spoon with a long handle, bent into a "U" turn at the end, hanging on a wire above the crusty, antique coffee pot. "Don't tell me that guests use that spoon to stir their coffee?"

"I don't think guests use it, but plumbers sure do."

Larry poured coffee into their two tiny white cups all the way to the brim. It was a delicate balancing act. By filling the cup to the tippy top, the risk of spillage was high. But if the cup was filled to a spill-free level, the coffee was a six swallow cup. Larry carefully handed Susan her cherished reward. "Based on your comment about the community spoon, I will assume you're drinking your coffee black."

Susan wryly smiled, but said nothing.

Larry continued, "Since I don't want to wear my coffee, I always take a couple of sips before I start walking."

"I think if I owned a supply house I would upgrade the coffee area, even if I had to charge for coffee."

"Plumbers come here for the free coffee and donuts. If they were going to pay for it, they'd go to Caffeine Sally's."

Susan set down her cup. "I suppose you're right."

After pausing, Susan remembered the promotional item in the back seat of the van. "Larry, we left the coffee maker in the van. I didn't think much of it until I saw what it's replacing. I'll set it up while you go about your business."

"You're the best helper ever. Thanks. I'll be back in a bit."

After saying quick hellos to all the countermen who were busy servicing plumbers, Larry headed into the office where he was immediately greeted by Jimmy. "Damn, Larry. You are not making any friends. Red is pissed off at you and so is Mr. P."

"It's great seeing you here bright and early, Jimmy."

Since Marsha was not in this early, Larry headed down the long hall and stuck his square head into the doorway of Russ Petersen's office.

"Good morning. Have a seat, Larry."

Larry sat down, took a sip of coffee and smiled. "Well, first off, I want to apologize for the delay in shipping your order."

"You didn't need to come here to tell me that, but I'm glad to see you. Independence better not hold up my order because of credit! Did you tell these people that I always pay my bill promptly?"

"Yes I did. They know your credit record is impeccable. The delay is due to the factory's ramp up of California compliant product. But, the order is on its way."

Russ Petersen looked at Larry with a squinting, sideways, skeptical look. The silence made Larry uncomfortable. He deflected his gut churning uneasiness by taking the final sip from his six-sip cup. Russ opened a folder and handed Larry three purchase orders: one for 150 forty gallon heaters, another for 150 fifty gallon models and a third with a mixture of models. "Since your shipping is so bad, I'm ordering extra loads. Tell the factory to extend my billing thirty days! That's the least they can do."

Larry graciously accepted the orders. "Thank you very much Mr. P. I consider myself very fortunate to have you as a customer. By the way, I'm working on a major repair plumber in Los Angeles. If I can put a deal together, would you ship water heaters to a customer in L.A.?"

"Thanks Larry, but we don't ship to anyone outside of the Inland Empire."

"Don't you send a truck to L.A. to will-call from factory warehouses on Wednesdays?"

"Yes we do."

"Well, what if you filled your bob-tail with water heaters, delivered them to Silverman Plumbing, and then did your pick-ups?"

"Silverman Plumbing?"

"Yes sir!"

"You're putting together a deal with Silverman Plumbing?"

"Yes sir!"

"You never cease to amaze me Larry. You might be onto something there."

"Once Frank approves Silverman's program and Socrates shakes on a deal, we can take a ride to L.A. and have lunch with him at his restaurant."

"Socrates?"

"That's what I call Clarence."

"Clarence has a restaurant?"

"Yes sir. He and his brother own Mervin's Place."

"Mervin's Place?"

"Yes sir!"

"It just got a nice review in the LA Times. I'd love to have lunch with you and Clarence at Mervin's, and I'd love to sell him water heaters."

"Beautiful!"

Russ smiled. "Clarence and I had dinner at an industry function a few years ago. He's built quite an empire!"

"Yes, he has. Russ Petersen doing business with Clarence Silverman! Wow! That would be quite a coup."

"You have quite a way with theatrics and words. Perhaps you should pursue a career in Hollywood."

Larry grinned. "By the way, I brought you a present. Can I get you to come out to the counter to see it?"

Russ didn't say a word. He just got up and silently followed Larry. When Russ saw Susan, he smiled. "Susan is my present?"

"Well, not exactly, but check out the coffee maker that Independence sent you."

"Looks like they ship coffee machines better than they ship water heaters; maybe they're in the wrong business."

Larry ignored the comment, "You are now officially the first stocking distributor in Southern California."

Russ couldn't waste the opportunity to drop more coffee grinds into Larry's bag of jelly beans. "How did I become a stocking distributor without any inventory?"

Larry scratched his head and responded, "I think it would be appropriate for you to take the first sip out of your one-of-a-kind Independence coffee maker."

Even Russ Petersen couldn't resist that offer. "Susan, you make a great pot of coffee. It's obvious you are a doer. Since Larry can't get me my water heaters, perhaps you should step in and be my rep."

CHAPTER 21

"Larry Being Larry"

Susan had done it yet again. She had charmed one of Larry's hard-nosed customers. Being a woman helped. Being a beauty in a beast's world certainly worked to her advantage. But those qualities alone were not Susan's secret. It was her understated style and coy smile that did not invite flirtation, but subtly hinted at it. In the company of the male human species, Susan had a way of acting like she was just one of the boys, when it was obvious that she was not.

As Larry got behind the wheel of the Caravan, he quipped, "Welcome aboard!"

"Aboard what? Are we going on a cruise?"

"Yes, provided cruising around in my Caravan counts."

"Very funny, Larry."

"You won over Red, five years ago at the Flier's over a cup of coffee, and now Mr. P is in love with you. I couldn't help but notice the smile on his face as he sipped a drink from the coffee maker you set up for him. From the looks of it, you just picked up a new account in your career at Connection Sales."

"One salesman in the family is more than enough. That water heater coffee maker is hideous, but it sure beats the heck out of the crusty antique it replaced."

"I appreciate the help. Sorry, but I need to make a quick call."

At the next red light, Larry dialed Frank. "Good morning."

"I thought you had a doctor appointment."

"I do."

"Then why are you bothering me?"

A red neck driving a beat up F-350 with giant earth-mover tires, weaved around the Caravan. As he rode his horn, he saluted Larry with his middle finger. Larry was undeterred. "I'm not trying to be a bother, Frank. I just called to tell you how great it is to work for you and to find out if you approved the programs I faxed you."

"Mr. Jelly Bean, I will remind you that I'm a sales manager, not a miracle worker."

Larry ignored Frank's sarcasm. "I'm merely asking for your blessing of the critical programs necessary to get us new customers. I thought you hired me to sell water heaters."

While Larry skidded to a stop at an intersection, Frank continued, "Larry, its 7:15. Why do you continue to punish me by being my very last call on one day and the very first call the following morning? I regret to inform you that working through the entire night is not part of my program. As I told you about nine hours ago, I'll call you after I talk to Freddy."

Larry nervously tapped the gas and then the brake. "Who's Freddy?"

"That's my boss, Freddy Garagiola."

"I don't know anything about him. Wasn't there a baseball player with that name?"

Frank ignored the baseball comment even though he knew Larry was referring to Joe Garagiola, the famous Yankee turned broadcaster. He grumbled back a response, "Freddie knows a whole bunch about you. He asks me every day why I didn't hire an Italian rep. Trust me, everybody at Independence knows about Larry Schafer."

Larry, with one hand on the wheel, made a left hand turn at the signal, barely squeaking past oncoming traffic. "I'm not sure if that's good or bad."

"Their information comes from me. Keep bothering me and I'll quit telling them you're a great guy. Just remember, you can easily be replaced with a rep whose last name ends in a vowel. Get the picture?"

"It's a little fuzzy. I might need a new picture tube."

"On top of everything else, while you ramble on and on about nothing, you're racking up more minutes. Say good-bye and call me after you see the doctor. I'm eager to find out if your problems are really physical or if you're driving yourself and everybody else crazy because of major mental issues. What was it that your brother always told you when you were a kid?"

"Act normal?"

"Yes! Exactly! Act normal, Larry!"

"Good-bye Frank."

As Larry hung up the phone and regrouped, Susan exploded, "We need to take out some life insurance on you!"

Larry was frustrated. "First I get a bunch of crap from Frank, and now you. I'm pretty darn sure that Dr. Van Slyke is not going to give me a death sentence."

"I know that, Larry. I'm talking about your driving when you're on that phone. You are really scary. While you're talking, your mind is spinning out of control somewhere across the universe."

"I'm just taking care of business. Don't make a mountain out of a mole hill."

"Larry, you just drove over the top of the mole hill and nearly crashed us off the mountain. On top of that, we're lucky that truck driver didn't pull out a gun and shoot us both. We're lucky to be alive. I'm surprised mobile phones are legal to use while operating a vehicle. How do you expect to drive in this world when your brain is operating in another?"

"Stop exaggerating!"

"Exaggerating? I don't think so, Larry. While you're waging a war of words with a principal who is wondering why he hired you in the first place, the Caravan is on auto pilot. If you keep it up, even Frank will tell you to go to work for the pencil breaker."

"So you're telling me it should be against the law to talk on the phone while driving?"

"Yes!"

"That sounds just like a Democrat. The last time I checked, we are living in a free country."

Larry should have stopped himself. Why did he drag politics into the conversation? He braced himself for Susan's rebuttal, but it was not forthcoming. He kept glancing in her direction. Nothing! Just a heavy dose of stewing.

Susan continued her silence. She elected, in this case, to let Larry have the last word. Sometimes that was best. As they proceeded towards the medical center in Riverside, she soothed her mood by singing an old Beatles song to herself. 'Words are flowing out like endless rain into a paper cup.'

As Larry turned into the parking lot he smiled cautiously and made a peace offering, "It really worries me when you're quiet."

"Oh, I was just drifting across the universe. Remember that old Beatles song?"

Larry backed the van into a parking spot and answered, "What made your mind head in that direction?"

"I'm not sure, Larry. When my mind starts wandering, it chooses its own trail."

"Who's on that trail with you?"

"Charlie and Sergeant Pepper, of course."

"How about me?

"I invited you, but it appears you now reside in your own world, oblivious to me and everything else."

Larry, in an abrasive baritone of missed notes, sang the song out loud, "Words are flowing out like endless RAIN into a paper cup."

Susan laughed, "That is exactly why I fell in love with you. You sing just exactly like John Lennon!"

As they walked into the medical center, Susan slipped her hand into Larry's. She thought about their first walk across the Disneyland parking lot many, many silent treatments ago. Fortunately for Larry, Susan's silent treatments came in short spurts. And, when they were over, life was good again. They were like storms that blew over and gave way to bright sunshine.

While sitting in the waiting room, Larry wondered if this doctor appointment would once again lead to a hall pass. He was far too young to struggle merely putting one foot in front of the other.

He hungered for good news but at the same time feared it would be bad. He thought about all the dots that needed to be connected to get Independence Water Heaters launched. Based on the activities of the first few days, he was encouraged. It certainly had been a whirlwind ride. A week ago, he had two employees and was struggling to survive from the commissions earned selling PROH$_2$O faucets. Now, he was pioneering a new product in the water heater business, an industry that he knew very little about. Frank, his mentor and longtime friend, was in a new job with a new company and had little, to no discretionary time. Because of that, Frank provided on the job training for Larry in bits and pieces. Therefore, much of Larry's education came from his customers. If not for his well-nourished garden of contacts and trusted friends in the business, Larry would have been screwed. But, all in all, he was making progress. Good progress.

Susan had no idea that Larry's daydreams were more about Connection Sales and less about his inability to climb stairs without being out of breath. "Don't worry, Larry. It will be okay. Whatever the news from the doctor, we'll make the best of it. It doesn't really matter where our trail heads, we'll always have each other."

Now Larry did worry. But just for a moment, before snapping right out of it. "Let's go to the Flier's for breakfast after we see the doctor. What do you think?"

"Sure, Larry, but only if you treat. I didn't bring my purse."

A nurse opened the door and announced, "Laurenz Schafer!"

Larry looked at Susan, "That's me."

"I'd like to join you. Do you mind?"

While Larry wore an agreeable smile, the nurse permitted both of them entry. After the usual checklist of a blood pressure test and weigh-in, Larry and Susan found themselves in a small, stark office awaiting the arrival of Dr. Van Slyke.

After ten minutes that felt like an hour, the doctor arrived. "Looks like I've got two of you for the price of one."

Susan immediately replied, "I'm Larry's wife, Susan. I hope you don't mind me being here."

The all business doctor indicated that it would not be a problem. She then turned all of her attention towards Larry. "So tell me a bit about what's going on."

"Well, doctor, I know I'm fat and out of shape, but still, at my age, it doesn't seem like I should be walking like an old man. Also noteworthy, earlier this year, I joined a gym. I was really into it. I worked very hard to strengthen every muscle in my body. That went on for five or six weeks. I was frustrated because I was unable to increase the weight on any apparatus I was using. I was getting nowhere. The trainer was puzzled and so was my friend, Dr. David, a chiropractor in town."

Dr. Van Slyke studied Larry's file. "Alright, let's see what we can figure out. Looks like you've received referrals resulting in no apparent answers."

"Yes, so far all I get are hall passes that lead to dead-end trails."

The neurosurgeon balanced compassion with a need to defend her colleagues. "I understand, but the medical field is not an exact science."

After an awkward pause, the doctor continued, "You were born in 1951, which makes you 42 years old, correct?"

"Yes, that's right?"

"There's a note in your file that says you have issues climbing stairs. Please explain."

"Our barn also serves as my office. This week I moved downstairs because I'm unable to climb a flight of stairs without using a hand railing and gasping for air. I also have one heck of a time walking up the steep driveway at our home."

"I need to know a little bit about your history. How active were you as a child?"

"Well, I was the worst player on the team, but I did play high school football. I played all sports and was no better than average at any of them. However, what I lacked in skill, I made up for in determination. My claim to fame was being Igor Krakeldorf's tackling dummy."

Dr. Van Slyke let down her professional guard and smiled at Larry being Larry. "I'll let your last comment, pertaining to Igor, go without further questions."

"That's probably a wise decision, Doctor."

"So, Larry, can you tell me when you first noticed that something might be wrong?"

"Well, let me think. About three years ago I was playing softball. I hadn't really played the game very much since college. Anyway, I was playing left field. A ball came to me. I caught it on one bounce and saw that I had a play at home plate. I always had a strong arm, so I expected to nail the guy with a good throw."

Larry paused to muster up the courage to describe a crossroads in his life.

The doctor, in a consolatory voice, pushed Larry close to his breaking point, "So what happened Larry?"

In a quivering voice, Larry replied, "My throw barely made it to the shortstop. I was embarrassed and frustrated. I tried to shake it off as me just being out of shape. But deep down inside, I knew better."

"You mentioned Dr. David. So you are a frequent visitor to the chiropractor?"

"Unfortunately, yes. I tend to throw my back out."

"When did that start?"

"About twenty years ago. I hopped a fence, landed awkwardly and ended up pretty messed up. That's when I became familiar with chiropractic adjustments."

"When was the last time you had a major back problem?"

"Actually, yesterday. If it weren't for the red carpet special, I might not have made this appointment."

"Pardon me."

"Never mind, it's really not important."

"I think you should let me be the judge of that."

Larry explained his ordeal on Highway 126 and how he rolled like a ball at the Dodge dealership.

Dr. Van Slyke took a deep breath. She smiled, and showed a glimpse of being amused, but tried hard not to show it. However, in spite of Larry once again being Larry, she maintained her unrelenting focus. The neurosurgeon was like a detective trying to get to the heart of a tough case. "Susan, what observations do you have about Larry's physical condition?"

"Well, for one thing, he's always had an interesting walk."

Larry interjected, "Some of my contractor friends call me Ratchet-Ass."

"Ratchet-Ass?"

"Yes."

"What do you do for a living, Larry?"

"I'm an independent sales agent in the plumbing industry."

"That probably explains why you're not offended by your nickname. In your business, I would think you need to have thick skin and a sense of humor."

Larry answered in the third person, "I think that's how Larry became Larry."

The doctor changed direction, heading down a different trail. "Perhaps I should get a look at that walk, Larry. If you don't mind, let's come out here in the hallway. Please walk to the end of the hall in your normal way and then return."

The doctor watched Larry walk down the hall and then back. She then asked Larry to repeat the demonstration. As he again walked down the stark hall, he was embarrassed. Being ridiculed by ball-busting plumbers didn't bother him, but showcasing his stride down the hall of a medical office felt awkwardly demeaning. In his mind, ridicule was okay; being on display was not. He also worried that the doctor was onto something that would be bad news.

As the neurosurgeon watched the final steps of the routine, she shook her head in a quiet affirmation. Susan watched the doctor study her husband and was convinced that she had solved the puzzle that was Larry. Dr. Van Slyke closed her eyes and breathed deeply before summoning the Schafers into her private office. As Larry followed Susan and the doctor, he nervously sensed that this doctor would not be issuing a hall pass.

The doctor invited Larry and Susan Schafer to have a seat across from her desk. After a silent moment that allowed them to settle into their chairs, she gathered every ounce of strength she could muster up, removed her reading glasses and looked Larry directly in the eye. "I will confirm my diagnosis with a muscle biopsy, but I am fairly certain that you have Muscular Dystrophy."

Larry and Susan squirmed quietly while trying to understand how the doctor's diagnosis would affect their lives; their world; their universe. A terrifying reality silenced the room. The doctor was dressed in a white gown that matched the pale starkness of the faces that sat before her.

It was unclear which emotion was more prevalent in the minds of the Schafers: dumbfounded confusion or the startled fear of an incomprehensible life changer. Larry's lip quivered and his eyes moved randomly, trying to regain focus. Susan grabbed his shaking hand and squeezed it lovingly tight.

The neurologist's mission was to calm her emotions. Failing that attempt, she scrambled to find the courage to move ahead anyway. "There are many varieties of Muscular Dystrophy. Based on our discussion and my observation, it appears that you have Limb Girdle Muscular Dystrophy."

Larry took a deep regrouping breath and exhaled ever so slowly. "How did this disease find me?"

"LGMD is a rare muscle disorder that can only be inherited if the disease is present in the genetic make-up of both parents. Larry, you are not a one in a million, but you're real close."

Larry always had a feeling he was not normal. Perhaps a one in the million as the doctor said. He was reminded that he was not normal by his family and friends on a routine basis. While organizing his thoughts, Larry blurted out a random question that was not critical to his newly discovered challenge, "I hear conversation about Multiple Sclerosis on the news. Are the diseases related?"

"The two diseases are confused because the names sound similar, but there is no connection between them."

Since Larry's back still shot spurts of pain up and down his body from yesterday's episode at the gas station, he asked, "Is muscular dystrophy causing the back problems that have plagued me most of my life?"

"My guess is that your back problems are linked to weakness in the muscles that are charged with keeping your spine properly aligned. Therefore, albeit indirectly, your back issues are likely tied to Limb Girdle Muscular Dystrophy."

Susan hoped for the best, but feared the worst. Would she become a caretaker for her physically challenged husband? The avid reader and realist was committed to eliminating variables. "Is Lou Gehrig's disease related to muscular dystrophy?"

The neurosurgeon again responded, "Actually yes, Lou Gehrig's disease, also called ALS, is in the muscular dystrophy family of diseases. It rapidly debilitates victims. If there is any good news here, I would tell you that Limb Girdle Muscular Dystrophy is much slower moving."

Larry worried about Susan. In their wedding vows she did say "I do", but living with a crippled husband was far beyond the call of duty. Larry searched for illumination at the end of a darkening tunnel, but so far, not even a crack of light shone. He grasped for good news on a bad news day. Were there any jelly beans in the freshly opened bag of thorns? Were there any dots that were connectable? He was determined to get to the heart of the matter. He was hopeful, but instinctively knew the answer to a critical question, "What is the treatment for Limb Girdle Muscular Dystrophy?"

Dr. Van Slyke's head dropped in slow motion as her fingers tapped randomly on her desk. After moving her head back to eye level, she clasped her hands as if she was wringing every drop of moisture out of a wet rag. She then delivered more bad news, "Unfortunately, there is no cure."

Silence once more took the stage. Larry found it more difficult to swallow. Words that usually streamed from his mouth like a raging river, were dry docked. Finally he commented, "My brother doesn't have it."

"Sounds like he's the lucky one."

Larry thought about his childhood. He really never was normal. He thought about his inability to do even one "chin-up", while his brother lifted himself up and down from the gymnastics bar like a well-greased piston. Did this explain why he was no more than a tackling dummy for Igor Krakeldorf on the high school football team?

As it was in many families, common thinking amongst family and friends was that Larry, the younger brother, was pampered and Otto, the big brother, was taken to task on almost everything. Larry secretly knew it was true. The fact of the matter was that growing up in an immigrant family was not easy for either one of them, or their parents. But, when compared with Otto, Larry did have it easy. Now the pendulum of life had swung the other direction, as if to counter balance.

With a shaky voice, Susan commented, "This is the disease that Jerry Lewis raises money for in his telethon, correct?"

The doctor responded, "Yes."

Larry hated being cornered into a real world that provided few options. But still, he wanted to know the facts. "Jerry's kids on the telethon wear braces on their legs or are mobile only in wheel chairs. Their struggle to move their arms and legs is heart tugging. Is that where I'm headed?"

"Well, first off, we will need the results of the biopsy to confirm my diagnosis."

Larry refused to let the doctor off the hook that easily, so he made a no-nonsense comment, "Let's assume you're right."

After yet another deep breathe the doctor continued, "The disease weakens the muscles in your arms, legs and torso at more or less a constant rate from the time of birth. Since you're being diagnosed later in life, your prognosis is likely to be better than the kids you see on TV."

"Will I end up spending my life in a wheel chair?"

The neurologist paused to gather the right words to answer a question that had no sure answer. "That's hard to say, but based on your age and how you are getting around now, I would say you'll be okay for a while."

Since Larry was not comfortable in gray areas, he continued, "So there's no time line available?"

There was no way to sugarcoat an answer for that question. The doctor's intent was to answer the question calmly, but in a real world that can be harsh, she remarked with a painful stutter, "Unfortunately not."

Larry had spent a lifetime connecting dots. Dealing with a random un-connectable dot, called Limb Girdle Muscular Dystrophy, scared the hell out of him. He had always been a solution finder. A problem solver. A dot connector. A master at converting challenges into opportunities. A clever angle finder that simplified the complex. In his world, the *Jelly Beans in Life* always prevailed. But now what? He was at a loss for words.

As for Susan, she had learned that Larry was not normal when she first met him at Ventura College twenty three years earlier. Growing up, Otto frequently implored his brother to act normal. Was it possible that Larry traveled through his life blazing trails that others never considered because he had an ailment that was anything but normal? After all, according to the doctor, he was literally a one in a million.

Was it possible that in some crazy way, Larry, without knowing he had the disease that lived within him, compensated for it by harnessing, from deep within actions that at times came right out of left field? Was it those resources that often drove the people that he cared most about to the edge of insanity, while other times acting as a bonding catalyst? Or was this a revelation? In some twisted way, did muscular dystrophy explain, Larry being Larry?

Dr. Van Slyke sat quietly. Only experience can prepare doctors for brutally tough conversations like this. Communicating good news is fun and easy. As for bad news, that's altogether different. She wondered if she had been successful at making something she knew was a life changer, sound like really no big deal at all.

Larry and Susan sat in a daze. Surely there were many more questions to ask, but the Schafers were mentally spent and emotionally exhausted.

The doctor let the conversation take its course amidst silent intervals. "I can only imagine how you feel. Is there anything else that I might be able to help you with?"

Two weary souls shook their heads. "No".

There was yet another block of silence before the doctor continued, "Larry, you will be receiving an appointment card in the mail for your biopsy. Don't schedule too much after the procedure. The incision will be on your thigh; four to five inches long. To help you through the discomfort, a pain prescription will be available for pick-up at the pharmacy."

Larry thanked the doctor as he shook her hand. Susan was gracious and polite. Not a word was spoken on their way to the car. Larry was grasping for resolve. Susan was in survival mode, hunkering down while the storm passed through.

CHAPTER 22

"Across the Universe"

A brief moment after Larry cranked the van's ignition, his phone rang. A quick trip to reality put him right back into business mode. "Larry, this is Frank. When you check your fax machine, you'll find the program approvals you requested."

The positive news allowed Larry to set aside the eight ball that Dr. Van Slyke had just deposited into the corner pocket of his life. "Great, great news. Thank you!"

"What did the doctor have to say?"

Larry had not developed a plan on how he would deal with the diagnosis, let alone how he would tell his family and friends, or if he would tell them at all. But in Frank's case, Larry reacted as if he were on auto-pilot. It was yet another example of Larry being Larry. He fired back an answer more like a machine than a human being struggling to cope, "The doctor said I have muscular dystrophy. I'm officially one of Jerry's kids."

"Are you serious, or is this a ploy to sucker me into giving you more strokes on the golf course?"

Larry followed yet another silent moment while he found the words to respond, "This is for real."

Since Frank was a frequent participant in the world of Larry being Larry, he responded without hesitation, "Okay. Here's the deal. Short term, I'll give you one more stroke a side. Long term, I'll find someone to haul your fat ass around to see your customers. If you play your cards right, it'll be a good looking blond or red head. I'll let you pick. Don't tell Susan. It'll be our secret."

Frank made Larry laugh for the first time in what seemed like an eternity. "You're on speaker phone Frank, and Susan is with me."

Susan, not wanting to change the mood of a conversation that, given the circumstances, was anything but normal, graciously entered the world of Larry being Larry. "Hi Frank. No worries. I like the idea of Larry having a good looking chauffer. It would take the pressure off of me."

"Larry, you are one lucky man. If I ever found a woman like Susan, I'd get married."

Susan continued the fantasy-like game. "Hang in there Frank, Larry is on probation. If he doesn't shape up, I'll be available."

Larry's mind was still playing the jelly bean game. "We're on our way to the Flier's. Do you want to join us?"

Frank didn't hesitate, "I'm on my way."

When struggling through a crossroads in life, it can be advantageous to push reality aside and allow happiness to intrude. This was one of those times. The world of Larry being Larry, in a fantasy jelly bean world, was the right medicine at the right time. Susan grabbed Larry's hand. "It'll be okay. You are blessed to have lots of friends and family that care about you."

Larry smiled, "The Beatles, right?"

"Yes! 'With a little help from my friends'."

"That's it!"

The phone rang again. "Larry, will I be getting the Ray Brown special?"

"Hi John, actually I just talked to Frank. He faxed me a proposal to present to you. However, I haven't seen it yet."

"I don't want a proposal. I want the Ray Brown special. Remember, I know how much it costs to manufacture a water heater. When will you get around to reading your faxes?"

"Tonight, John. I'll call you in the morning."

"Better yet, come up to Lancaster. I'll spring for the venti latte, cannoli, and even include a CD!"

Larry stayed on the imaginary trail he and John were traveling. "That's a tough offer to turn down, but is there any chance I can trade the Ray Brown CD for a Diana Krall?"

"You drive a very tough bargain, Larry, but I'll concede to your counter-offer. There's a new Diana Krall album that just came out. If you play your cards right, I might be able to get my hands on it."

"That would be amazing! See you in the morning, John!"

Larry hung up the phone. Suddenly, he was tired of the charade. He vowed not to answer the phone again, regardless of who was calling.

Susan shook her head. "Is this your life now? You drive around all corners of the universe talking on the phone? Is this the next chapter of Larry being Larry?"

"Pretty much, but I'm done with it for now."

Susan took a slow, deep breath before responding in frustration, "I'm not sure if that phone is a blessing or a curse."

"I guess it depends on who's calling me."

Larry pulled into the Flier's parking lot and easily connected two dots that were no-brainers. "That's Red's truck!"

Susan added, "And that's Sam's '53 Chevy!"

As Larry and Susan got out of the Caravan, the Santa Ana winds kicked up. Calm was replaced with turbulence. Dust and sand began blowing wildly. The Schafers hustled in to find Mayor Sam having a late breakfast with Red and Mary. Since Mary had been fighting digestive problems, the friends were discussing the virtues of Sam's beloved Dr. 'M'.

The accidental meeting was greeted with an explosion of laughter and happiness. Red took charge by getting the attention of Candy who, after Larry laid her off, was back at the Flier's waiting tables. "Looks like we're now a group of five."

Susan added, "Make that six. Frank is on his way."

As tables, chairs and a maze of table settings were reconfigured, Larry's mind circled back to Dr. Van Slyke's diagnosis. Muscular dystrophy. Larry had Limb Girdle Muscular Dystrophy. There was no cure and very little chance that his life would ever have any semblance of normalcy. But, then again, since the disease was programmed into him at conception, he never was normal. What would his life with the crippling disease become? Larry Schafer disdained the thought of anyone feeling sorry for him. It was very difficult for him to request help for anything. He cherished his independence. Would this disease suddenly make him dependent?

How about all those dots. Would the debilitating disease prevent him from making the necessary connections required to keep his business viable? He thought again. He might be okay short term, but for how long? And of course Susan. It was one thing to put up with a ratchet-ass, but now?

Susan shook Larry, "Hello, are you there? Anybody home?"

Larry was startled by the abrupt return to the real world. Susan took a big breath and exhaled ever so slowly, "Guess what, Larry?"

"We're going home?"

"No Larry. I was just going to tell you how lucky we are."

"So we are going home?"

"Not a chance. Our closest friends have converged here at the Flier's as though, from across the universe, our master made it so."

Larry was venturing down an untraveled trail, far beyond Larry being Larry. On this trail, Larry had lost his ability to assess and regroup. Time and place, momentarily had become, at best, blurry. He wasn't sure, but it didn't look like they were returning to the ranch. He whispered to Susan, "Why can't we have this discussion with Sergeant Pepper and Charlie?"

"Larry, you're acting like a freshman in my English literature class after I call them to my desk to explain why they failed to turn in their Hamlet assignment. You're not acting like Larry at all. We are among friends."

"I need to figure stuff out. I don't want to ruin breakfast for our friends and I don't want pity."

"So you don't want anyone to feel sorry for you. Is that the idea?"

"Exactly."

"Are you giving up on life or your friends?"

"Neither. I just think that I need to connect some dots. Pity for me, I think, is pitiful."

"The friends we have will provide compassion, not pity!"

"When I look into their eyes, how will I differentiate compassion from pity?"

"The spirit in their heart will make it obvious."

Larry paused before replying, "What happened to the realist I married?"

"I think that she traded places with the romantic that she married."

Larry was struggling to make sense of anything. "So now what?"

"I'm absolutely certain that I'll regret saying these words, but perhaps it's time for Larry to be Larry."

Larry was bewildered. "I just need to create a roadmap; a game plan; a trail guide. With a little time to myself, a yellow pad, and a sharp pencil, maybe I can do that."

Susan wondered what trail Larry's mind was blazing. It seemed as though he had put the world on time out. Was he in shock? Had he temporarily lost his mind? How could she reel him back from wherever his lost heart and soul had traveled?

Larry's attention now turned to Frank, who had found the inner strength to steady himself, acting like he knew nothing when in fact he knew everything. No words were exchanged, but, for a brief moment, his mere presence and quiet confidence calmed Larry, his mind searching for the *Jelly Beans in Life*. Where were they?

We are what we are. But sometimes, in times of crises, we become something that we typically are not. Larry the romantic had turned into a bewildered, depressed realist. Susan's reaction, not by some grand plan, but by instinct, was a reinvention. Magically, Susan, the realist and Larry, the romantic, had exchanged roles.

Susan squeezed Larry's hand as he commented, "The doctor said that I'm traveling down a dead-end trail of unknown length."

Susan shook her head. "Maybe. Maybe not. Mayor Sam found a miracle on 12th Street."

Larry was puzzled. "What?"

"You act confused."

"That's because I am. A miracle on 12th Street?"

Susan confidently replied, "Yes! Don't you remember Mayor Sam's Dr. M, on 12th street? Did you think that miracles occur only on 34th Street?"

"Well, I was sitting here struggling with the idea that miracles are on back order, just like water heaters."

"Join me Larry, travel across the universe with me. Perhaps it will lead us to a trail that is not a dead end."

Larry did not reply. He was quiet. Not because he didn't want to join Susan, suddenly the romantic, but because his head was spinning. He fidgeted and forced a smile that was obviously manufactured. He loved Susan for trying so darn hard to make him feel better; to revitalize his spirit; to tear down the barrier he had built between him and the friends that meant so much to him, the very friends that he did not want to burden with his problems.

After stewing a bit more, Larry found the inner strength to tackle the connection of the biggest dots in his life. He took a deep breath and resolved to improvise. He would move ahead even without a sharp pencil and yellow pad. He turned his paper placemat upside down, exposing a white blank canvas. He then grabbed a child's sharp crayon from a small bucket on the table. How to start the thought process? That was the challenge. That very first notation on a blank slate always had a chance to set a possible course down a possible trail. Larry entered a zone, blocking out all distractions. He entered a world where only he existed. He shook his head in affirmation and wrote down the number '42'. That was his age. He paused and then he wrote the number '80'. The ashes of Larry's father were released at the ranch gazebo when Papa was 80 years old. Larry guessed he would be on a similar track.

Larry thought to himself that the challenge of muscular dystrophy was not only to travel from 42 to 80, but to travel the trail accomplishing as much as humanly possible by conquering the obstacles and detours on the trail along the way. Nothing would stop him from being a doer. He would continue to explore adventures and experience life to the fullest. Probably a little slower, but even plodders eventually reach their destination. Because Larry had already adapted to being athletically inept, no adjustment was required there. He would probably go from mediocre to horrible on the golf course, and his golf bag would probably get more difficult to carry. But those things would work themselves out. Dignity? When one's nickname is Ratchet-Ass, there is precious little dignity remaining to be lost. So he resolved to get over it. Respect? That was earned. He vowed to maintain every ounce of respect he had earned and set a goal to deposit additional ounces into his account.

Larry affirmed he had the resources: friends, family, and a spirit not easily deterred. He vowed to make a mark on the world that would live well beyond his existence on this earth. That was it. He would have a laser focus on accomplishing goals, even if he required some help. Larry was always quick to provide help and slow to ask for it. That was something that over time might change, but he vowed to continue to help wherever he could. He would not get burdened with how his goals would be accomplished. After all, except for strength in his muscles, he possessed the resources to travel any and all trails available to accomplish his goals. He further committed to help those that needed far more help than he ever would, provided they appreciated a helping hand. That was it. That was the 42-80 plan. Yes! 42-80!

Red glanced at the two numbers Larry had written with red crayon. He then interrupted Larry's mind travel, "Ratchet! Are you there? Let me help you out!"

Larry raised his head and smiled. "Sorry, I was just thinking."

"When you think, Ratchet, I worry."

Larry responded silently. Words were replaced with rolling eyes, a deep breath, and a puzzled smile.

Red continued, "Damn it Ratchet, it's not that hard. The answer is 61."

Larry was confused. Usually he confused Red, but now Red was confusing him. The only response Larry could muster up was weak; very weak, "Really?"

Red replied, "Of course! If you meet the truck halfway, you arrive at 61."

The eyes of Susan, Red, Frank, Mary, and Sam now focused on Larry's crayon numbers, written boldly on the back of the paper placemat.

Frank noted Larry needed some help, "Larry the number 61 is exactly halfway between 42 and 80. Is that what you're trying to figure out, for no apparent reason?"

Larry suddenly realized that the two numbers he had written on the placemat had opened the door for any number of interpretations that could lead to any number of trails and scores of destinations. Larry was happy that his friends had gone down an unintended trail. Hence, he would not need to explain the real meaning of the numbers and the details of his secret travel down a trail in the deep recesses of his own universe.

Larry responded with a lie, "Exactly! The answer is 61. For some reason I just couldn't make the numbers work. Thanks a bunch!"

The table was set. Candy, anticipating a handsome tip, cheerfully filled coffee cups. Mary added a splash of milk to her coffee to make her smile and a sprinkle of sugar to make her sweet. Susan followed suit. Mayor Sam, as part of his program designed by the mysterious Dr. M, added soy milk to his coffee. Red, Larry, and Frank drank their coffee black.

A giant tumbleweed rolled past the Flier's front window to find its own trail. Splashes of sunlight filtered through a row of cypress trees while a mighty gust of wind slammed the front door shut. Red held Mary's hand secretly under the table while Mayor Sam pulled on his red suspenders; studying the menu in search of a healthy entre. Frank fidgeted a bit, not knowing who knew what, aiming to set an example of confident control by acting like the duck that looked calm above the water while paddling like hell beneath it. He really wished he was not at the Flier's, but knew he had to be. Larry acknowledged Frank's confident demeanor, made eye contact with him and cracked half a smile.

Red interrupted the awkward moment, "So Ratchet, tell us all about your doctor appointment. Were you given a prescription to kick off your boots and wiggle your toes?"

All eyes were on Larry. He smiled a more genuine smile than the one he had been wearing. "Well, to begin with, you guys need to know how important you are to me. I'm incredibly lucky to have friends like you.

I'm humbly fortunate and thankfully blessed."

Larry paused, and continued, "If Susan will meet my jelly bean truck halfway, I'll travel through the universe with her."

Red turned towards his friends and bluntly asked, "What in the hell did Ratchet just say?"

A teary eyed Susan answered the question with compassionate resolve, "Don't worry Red, that was just Larry being Larry."

ACKNOWLEDGEMENTS

This book would not be possible without the help of my team of "BOOK BUDDIES" who inspire me, keep me straight, and roll up their sleeves when I need help. This teamwork ensures my books are the best they can be. My hope is that I've created a literary keepsake that readers enjoy and recommend to others.

Beverly Schmalhofer
Chief Editor who keeps me grounded

Patti Plummer
MGA2

Joe Notte
MGA2

Carrie and Peggy @ Author's Marketing Experts
Marketing wizards that connect readers to my books

Mike and Linda Edmonds
Pre-readers and this author's biggest fans

Bruce Carnevale
Industry Consultant

Bob Russak
A Jelly Beans fan who guides me through legalities

Lisa Rogal
Facebook administrator

Dan Rogal
Website Designer

Andrea Douglas
Administrator

Mike Bowerman
Chapter artwork for Jelly Beans in Life

Arron Sanders
Amazon connection